Teacher's Edition

Science

PEARSON
Scott
Foresman

Grade Pre-K Teacher's Edition

Editorial Offices: Glenview, Illinois • Parsippany, New Jersey • New York, New York
Sales Offices: Boston, Massachusetts • Duluth, Georgia • Glenview, Illinois
Coppell, Texas • Sacramento, California • Mesa, Arizona

ISBN: 0-328-23438-9

Copyright © 2008 Pearson Education, Inc.

All Rights Reserved. Printed in the United States of America. This publication is protected by Copyright, and permission should
be obtained from the publisher prior to any prohibited reproduction, storage in a retrieval system, or transmission in any form
by any means, electronic, mechanical, photocopying, recording, or likewise. For information regarding permission(s), write to:
Permissions Department, Scott Foresman, 1900 East Lake Avenue, Glenview, Illinois 60025.

1 2 3 4 5 6 7 8 9 10 V001 15 14 13 12 11 10 09 08 07 06

Start children on their learning journey.

Give your early learners a sure advantage. Scott Foresman Pre-K introduces preschoolers to the joys of learning with fun, engaging activities and age-appropriate science that starts them on their way toward success in learning.

Teacher's Edition

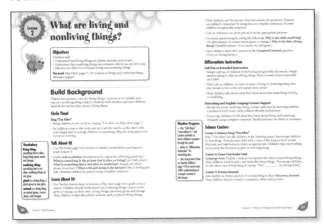

Big Books

Student Edition Flip Chart

Activities

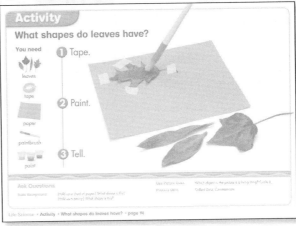

Activity

What shapes do leaves have?

You need

leaves

tape

paper

paintbrush

paint

① Tape.

② Paint.

③ Tell.

Ask Questions

Life Science • Activity • What shapes do leaves have? • page 14

...ving things?

Picture Clues   What are some things in the picture that are living, or alive? Circle each thing. What are some things that are nonliving? Put an X on those things.

...npare/Contrast   How are plants and animals alike?

Equipment Kit with Activity Placemats and Tray

Annie, the Dinosaur Puppet

Science Songs CD   **Giant Floor Puzzles**

Introduce children to the world of science.

With Scott Foresman Pre-K, young learners will discover the delights of science with plenty of learning opportunities.

Annie, the Dinosaur Puppet
Animate your lessons and songs with this plush puppet that children will love to have in the classroom.

The Little Red Hen

ADDISON-WESLEY

Vocabulary

living thing: something that is alive; living things grow, move and change.

nonliving thing: something that is not alive; nonliving things do not grow.

plant: is a living thing; a plant grows in one place.

animal: is a living thing; an animal grows, moves about, and changes.

Big Books

Read to your class from these three giant books (one Life Science theme, one Earth Science theme, and one Physical Science theme) that will surely captivate children's attention.

Vocabulary

Introduce new words and guide oral vocabulary development by asking children questions that engage them in dialogue.

Make learning fun!

Lots of exciting activities—from puzzles to sing-alongs—
introduce beginning science concepts in a motivating setting.

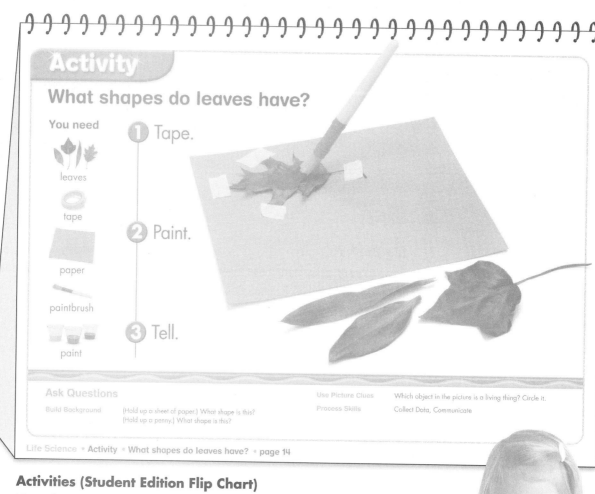

Activity

What shapes do leaves have?

You need

leaves

tape

paper

paintbrush

paint

1 Tape.

2 Paint.

3 Tell.

Ask Questions

Build Background   (Hold up a sheet of paper.) What shape is this?
                    (Hold up a penny.) What shape is this?

Use Picture Clues   Which object in the picture is a living thing? Circle it.

Process Skills   Collect Data, Communicate

Life Science • Activity • What shapes do leaves have? • page 14

Activities (Student Edition Flip Chart)
Keep class time interesting with an activity located after every three
or four lessons. The Activity Kit includes many of the materials needed
for each activity, a teacher's guide, and activity placemats.

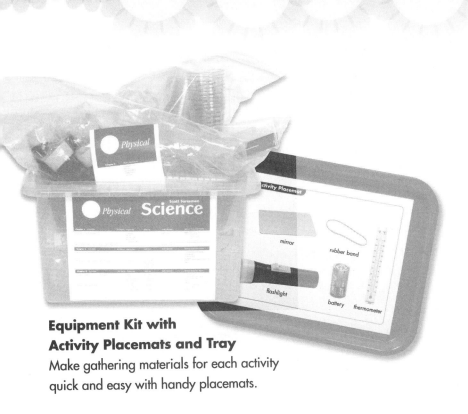

Equipment Kit with Activity Placemats and Tray

Make gathering materials for each activity quick and easy with handy placemats.

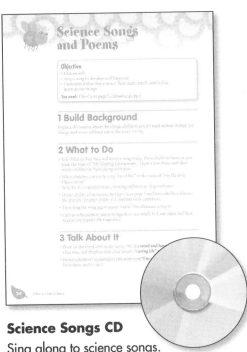

Science Songs CD

Sing along to science songs. Children will recognize familiar tunes and enjoy the fun science lyrics on this CD. One CD includes both lyrics and instrumental music for nine songs.

Giant Floor Puzzle

Get set for interactive fun! This colorful 24" x 36" puzzle will keep children amused while they are learning, whether they work as a group, in pairs, or even individually.

Authors

Dr. Timothy Cooney
Professor of Earth Science and Science Education
University of Northern Iowa (UNI)
Cedar Falls, Iowa

Dr. Jim Cummins
Professor
Department of Curriculum Teaching,
and Learning
University of Toronto
Toronto, Canada

Dr. James Flood
Distinguished Professor of Literacy and Language
School of Teacher Education
San Diego State University. San Diego State University
San Diego, California

Barbara Foots
Science Education Consultant
Houston, Texas

Dr. M. Jenice Goldston
Associate Professor of Science Education
Department of Elementary Education Programs
University of Alabama
Tuscaloosa, Alabama

Dr. Shirley Gholston Key
Associate Professor of Science Education
Instruction and Curriculum Leadership Department
College of Education
University of Memphis
Memphis, Tennessee

Dr. Diane Lapp
Distinguished Professor of Reading and Language Arts in Teacher Education
San Diego State University
San Diego, California

Sheryl Mercier
Classroom Teacher
Dunlap Elementary School
Dunlap, California

Dr. Karen Ostlund
Director
UTeach, College of Natural Sciences
The University of Texas at Austin
Austin, Texas

Dr. Nancy Romance
Professor of Science Education & Principal Investigator
NSF/IERI Science IDEAS Project Charles E. Schmidt College of Science
Boca Raton, Florida

Dr. William Tate
Chair and Professor of Education and Applied Statistics
Department of Education
Washington University
St Louis, Missouri

Dr. Kathryn C. Thornton
Professor
School of Engineering and Applied Science
University of Virginia
Charlottesville, Virginia

Dr. Leon Ukens
Professor or Science Education
Department of Physics, Astronomy, and Geosciences
Towson University
Towson, Maryland

Steve Weinberg
Consultant
Connecticut Center for Advanced Technology
East Hartford, Connecticut

Reviewers

Dr. Maria Aida Alanis
Administrator
Austin ISD
Austin, Texas

Melissa Barba
Teacher
Wesley Mathews Elementary
Miami, Florida

Dr. Marcelline Barron
Supervisor
Fairfield Public Schools
Fairfield, Connecticut

Jane Bates
Teacher
Hickory Flat Elementary
Canton, Georgia

Billie Bell
Teacher
Kansas City Missouri School District
Kansas City, Missouri

Denise Bizjack
Teacher
Dr. N. H. Jones Elementary
Ocala, Florida

Latanya D. Bragg
Teacher
Davis Magnet School
Jackson Mississippi

Richard Burton
Supervisor
George Buck Elementary School
Indianapolis, Indiana

Dawn Cabrera
Teacher
E.W.F. Stirrup School
Miami, Florida

Barbara Calabro
Teacher
Compass Rose Foundation
Fort Myers, Florida

Lucille Calvin
Teacher
Weddington Math & Science School
Greenville, Mississippi

Martha Cohn
Teacher
An Wang Middle School
Lowell, Massachusetts

Stu Danzinger
Supervisor
Community Consolidated School District 59
Arlington Heights, Illinois

Esther Draper
Science Specialist
Belair Math Science Magnet School
Pine Bluff, Arkansas

Sue Esser
Teacher
Loretto Elementary
Jacksonville, Florida

Dr. Richard Fairman
Professor
Antioch University
Yellow Springs, Ohio

Cecelia Ferguson
Teacher
School District of Lee County
Fort Myers, Florida

Joan Goldfarb
Teacher
Indialantic Elementary
Indialantic, Florida

Deborah Gomes
Teacher
A J Gomes Elementary
New Bedford, Massachusetts

Linda Halpin Walker
Teacher
McKinley-Brighton Magnet School
Syracuse, NY

Sandy Hobart
Teacher
Mims Elementary
Mims, Florida

Tom Hocker
Teacher/Science Coach
Boston Latin Academy
Dorchester, Massachusetts

Shelley Jaques
Science Coordinator
Moore Public Schools
Moore, Oklahoma

Marguerite W. Jones
Teacher
Spearman Elementary
Piedmont, South Carolina

Kelly Kenney
Teacher
Kansas City Missouri School District
Kansas City, Missouri

Carol Kilbane
Teacher
Riverside Elementary School
Wichita, Kansas

Robert Kolenda
Teacher
Neshaminy School District
Langhorne, Pennsylvania

Karen Lynn Kruse
Teacher
St. Paul the Apostle
Yonkers, New York

Elizabeth Loures
Teacher
Point Fermin Elementary School
San Pedro, California

Susan MacDougall
Teacher
Brick Community Primary Learning Center
Brick, New Jersey

Jack Marine
Teacher
Raising Horizons Quest Charter School
Philadelphia, Pennsylvania

Nicola Micozzi Jr.
Science Coordinator
Plymouth Public Schools
Plymouth, Massachusetts

Paula Monteiro
Teacher
A J Gomes Elementary
New Bedford, Massachusetts

Tracy Newallis
Teacher
Taper Avenue Elementary
San Pedro, California

Dr. Eugene Nicolo
Science Supervisor
Moorestown School District
Moorestown, New Jersey

Helen Pedigo
Teacher
Mt. Carmel Elementary
Huntsville, Alabama

Becky Peltonen
Teacher
Patterson Elementary School
Panama City, Florida

Sherri Pensler
Teacher
Claude Pepper Elementary
Miami, Florida

Virginia Rogliano
Teacher
Bridgeview Elementary
South Charleston, West Virginia

Debbie Sanders
Teacher
Thunderbolt Elementary
Orange Park, Florida

Grethel Santamarina
Teacher
E.W.F. Stirrup School
Miami, Florida

Migdalia Schneider
Teacher
Lindell School
Long Beach, New York

Susan Shelly
Teacher
Bonita Springs Elementary
Bonita Springs, Florida

Peggy Terry
Teacher
Madison District 151
South Holland, Illinois

Jane M. Thompson
Teacher
Emma Ward Elementary
Lawrenceburg, Kentucky

Martha Todd
Teacher
W. H. Rhodes Elementary
Milton, Florida

Renee Williams
Teacher
Central Primary
Bloomfield, New Mexico

Myra Wood
Teacher
Madison Street Academy
Ocala, Florida

Ms. Marion Zampa
Teacher
Shawnee Mission School District
Overland Park, Kansas

Using Scientific Methods for Science Inquiry

- To introduce the concept of scientific methods, tell children that they will learn about science by doing activities. Scientists do activities to understand how things around us are made and how they work. In activities we have to do things in steps, just as we do when we get ready for school in the morning: first we get dressed, then we eat breakfast, then we brush our teeth, and finally we go to school. The steps in an experiment are part of the scientific methods.

- Throughout the Scott Foresman Science program, the activities follow the steps of scientific methods. Children repeatedly use scientific methods as they complete the activities.

Ask a question.

The first step of any experiment is to ask a question about what we are trying to find out. By asking the question, **What happens when...?** we set an objective for the science activity.

Make your hypothesis.

Encourage children to tell what they think will happen. Help children express their own hypothesis or suggest a possible hypothesis for the whole class in the form of an **If.../then... statement**.

Control your variables.

Explain to children that as they do the activity, they will keep some things the same and change only one thing at a time. Then they will check whether their hypothesis is true or false.

Plan a fair test.

Explain to children the importance of repeating the "tests" they will be doing. Repeating an activity implies doing that activity over and over again, with a minimum of variation. This is how we make sure the results of tests are accurate and consistent.

Do your test.

Children can conduct tests by repeating an activity with a partner or in a small group with teacher guidance.

Collect and record your data.

An indispensable part of an activity is collecting and recording data. Children can dictate the information they observe. Talk about the different ways children can collect and record the results of their tests. Some examples might include making lists, charts, drawings, or graphs.

Tell your conclusion.

A conclusion answers the question "What did I learn?" To arrive at a conclusion, children will have to compare the results of the activity with their original hypothesis. Remind children of the hypothesis by asking the question, **"What did you think would happen when...?"** Tell children to check the results of the activity. Ask children if these results are what they had predicted before doing the tests. If they predicted the result, tell them the hypothesis was correct. If they did not, help them revise their hypothesis. Then help children form a conclusion.

Go further.

Sometimes children may want to follow a conclusion by testing and applying this newly acquired knowledge or by raising questions about related problems.

To guide children to further inquiry, suggest some other problems children might like to solve and ask questions.

Using Process Skills for Science Inquiry

- Tell children that scientists use what we call "process skills" when they are doing research. *Process skills* refer to the way scientists think about scientific problems. Like scientists, children will also use these skills when they do activities. Explain to children that when they test something, they are using process skills. When they collect and record data, they are using process skills. When they make conclusions and tell what they learned, they are using process skills.

Observe

One of the ways scientists can find out about an object or about how or why something happens is to observe that object or event.

Explain to children that to observe something, they must use at least one of their five senses. The five senses are seeing, hearing, smelling, touching, and tasting.

Communicate

Scientists communicate when they share what they know and learn. There are many ways to communicate. Discuss how speaking is a means of communicating. Show how using pictures, drawings, charts, and graphs are all ways to communicate.

Explain to children the importance of communicating: **If you want your friends to know something, you have to communicate with them. You have to tell them about it or show them what you want them to see or do.** Introduce the idea that observing and communicating are related. In order to communicate, people have to make use of some of their senses, such as seeing and hearing.

Classify

One more way for scientists to understand things around them is to organize things into groups. Many things or objects can be grouped together because they are similar in some way. These groups are then classified according to their characteristics (color, shape, size, function, and so on).

Estimate and Measure

Objects and events that we observe may have qualities or attributes that can be measured. Some qualities that can be measured are weight, length, capacity, loudness, time, and so on. Scientists use measurements to describe those qualities.

Explain to children that scientists measure things so that they can have more information about them. To measure things, we must choose a unit of measurement. Invite children to measure the length of an object in the classroom (for example, a book), using another object (such as a paper clip) as a unit of measure. Show how estimating differs from measuring by asking the children to estimate how long the book is: **How many paper clips do you think will fit on the book?** Then have the children use the paper clips to measure the book. Compare the results. Discuss why measuring is more accurate than estimating.

Infer

When we infer, we make a reasonable guess based upon observations or something we already know. For example, we can infer that it has rained from observing wet pavement and puddles of water.

Predict

Scientists may attempt to predict the results of an activity or how an object will react in certain conditions. Predicting requires us to state what we think will happen in the future. Predictions are based on past experiences. Ask children to predict what will happen to water when it is put in a freezer.

Make and Use Models

Scientists sometimes make models of objects or animals so that they can talk about them because some objects are too small or too large for people to observe easily.

Show children some examples of models such as a truck, car, and dinosaur. Ask children to tell something about the model that is the same as the real object and something that is different.

Make Definitions

A definition in science is a statement that makes clear the nature of a thing or the meaning of a word. Children can make a definition by describing something and telling what it means. Name some familiar objects and ask children to describe each object using their senses: **What color is it?**

What shape is it? Does it smell? Is it heavy? Is it light? Is it smooth or rough? Next, ask children to describe a familiar animal (cat, dog, bird) to a partner. Have children talk about as many things as they know about this animal without saying its name. Based on the description, have the partner guess the animal. Conclude by making a definition for the animal. (Possible answer: A cat purrs, makes a "meow" sound, and is a soft, furry animal. A cat has four legs, has whiskers, and a long tail.)

Make Hypotheses

Scientists must identify what it is they want to find out. This sets the course for all scientific investigations. Ask children to share other questions they may have thought of when completing an activity.

Collect and Record Data

Remind children there are many ways to organize their observations about an activity. The process of collecting data is an important step of the scientific methods. You can use pictures to collect data on a chart or graph. If possible, show children a simple pictograph. This will serve to show the value of recording information so that it can be shared over and over again.

Interpret Data

Tell children that after scientists have collected and recorded their data, or information, they have to interpret the data. When scientists interpret data, they study they results and compare them to decide what the data shows or means.

Plan a Fair Test

The process skill of planning a fair test is also described as a step in the Scientific Methods. Scientists plan a fair test when something changes in an activity while everything else stays the same.

Investigate and Experiment

Tell children that the process skills we call *investigate* and *experiment* are where we do the actual activity. We need to do the activity to find out whether our hypothesis is correct.

Safety in Science

Communicate to children that learning about science can be an exciting experience. However, it can also be a dangerous one if proper safety rules are not followed. Emphasize that conducting science activities requires an awareness of potential hazards and the need for safe practices. This means that appropriate safety procedures must be followed when completing scientific investigations.

Tell children that to have a safe year doing activities they must know important safety tips. Have children listen as you read each tip aloud. Then have them explain what they have learned about safety in science to a partner. Encourage children to add their own safety tips to a class list.

The following safety guidelines are provided for your information as you plan and implement the activities in this book.

- Stress to children the importance of listening carefully to your instructions.

- Be sure children always follow such safety rules as keeping a clean work area, never tasting substances without permission, wearing safety goggles or glasses, and safely handling glue, scissors, rulers, toothpicks, straws, and spools.

- Discuss with children the need to apply safe and appropriate techniques for handling, manipulating, and caring for materials, living organisms, scientific equipment, and technology. For example, children should identify ways to care properly for fish in an aquarium. Children should understand that fish need food and clean water and should be kept out of direct sunlight. Be sure that children understand that to protect native wildlife, they should not release living organisms into the environment. If necessary, biologists suggest freezing them in a sealed container and then disposing of the container.

Notes about Science Safety

- As children study the sky, they may be tempted to look straight into the Sun. Children should be aware that looking at the Sun without protective eyewear is dangerous. They should also be aware of the danger of Sun exposure and should use sunscreen.

- While talking about different kinds of sounds, children should be aware of the danger of exposure to sounds of high decibel levels. They should limit their exposure to such sounds, move farther away from the source of such sounds, or use protective ear wear.

- Talk with children about fire safety. Stress that only adults should handle matches or lighters. If a person's clothing catches on fire that person should *stop, drop*, and *roll*. They should never run.

- Be sure children understand the basic tools for gathering information. Discuss with children how to select the appropriate tools and use them safely.

- Remind children that water spills can be dangerous. Tell children to tell an adult when there has been a spill.

Science Tools

Children should be able to use appropriate tools and simple equipment/instruments to safely gather scientific data. Demonstrate each tool and its safe use as needed.

Goggles

Explain to children that it is essential they protect their eyes when performing certain activities. Safety goggles or safety glasses provide such protection. Demonstrate the use of safety goggles and discuss when they should be worn. Generate a class list of appropriate times.

Wind vane

Explain to children that a wind vane is a tool that can be used to determine which direction the wind is blowing. Wind vanes have a flat piece that turns around a rod and points in the same direction the wind is going. If you have access to a wind vane, demonstrate for children that it works best in a high, open space. A wind vane is also called a weather vane.

Hand lens

Demonstrate the safe use of a hand lens to children. Provide a variety of objects, including newspaper print, for children to examine using a hand lens. Ask children to describe how each object looks under the hand lens.

Clock

Make sure children know how to use a clock to tell time. Discuss how many minutes there are in an hour. Point out the second hand if the clock has one, and explain that there are 60 seconds in one minute.

Scissors

Explain to children that scissors are a tool used for cutting. Tell them that the scissors they will use to do science activities have safe, rounded edges, but they still need to be careful when handling scissors.

Measuring cup

Most scientists use containers marked with milliliters (mL) or cubic centimeters (cc). One mL equals one cc. Some measuring cups also provide customary units.

Ruler

Tell children that most rulers they will use provide both metric and customary units of length. A ruler is 12 inches (1 foot) or 30.48 centimeters long. Each centimeter is divided into 10 equal parts, or millimeters.

Explain to children that when they use a ruler, they should line up one end of the object they are measuring with the end of the ruler. Then they should look at the other end of the object and find the centimeter mark that is closest to it. Demonstrate how to measure using a ruler and a book.

Balance

Demonstrate the use of a balance to children. Have children practice measuring mass with a balance by first choosing two objects and predicting which one has more mass. Then have children put an object on each side of the balance. Have them observe which side of the balance is lower. Have them determine which object has more mass and explain their thinking.

Tuning fork

Have children lightly tap their desks with a tuning fork. Tell them to listen for the sound and feel the vibration. Explain to children that a tuning fork vibrates at a constant rate. Each tuning fork has a certain pitch. Pitch is how high or low a sound is. When scientists need a sound with a certain pitch, they can use a tuning fork.

Thermometer

Demonstrate to children the safe use of a thermometer. Point out the Fahrenheit (F) and Celsius (C) scales.

Have children measure temperature with a thermometer by doing the following activity. Put a thermometer in a cup of water. Have children observe the red line in the thermometer and record the temperature it indicates. Put the thermometer in a cup of warm water. Again have children observe the red line and record the temperature it indicates. Ask children to describe how the red line and the temperature changed.

Rain gauge

Tell children that a rain gauge is a tool scientists use for measuring how much rain has fallen. Set up a rain gauge in an open area for a week. Help children measure how much rain has fallen each day. At the end of the week, make a graph with the information and encourage children to make observations about each day's rainfall.

Magnet

Provide magnets, objects containing iron, and objects not containing iron for children to experiment with. Have them identify what objects contain iron and explain how they came to that conclusion. Have children place like and unlike poles together and observe the results.

Unit A Life Science

Introduce the Unit

- Introduce the unit of Life Science by showing children Flip Chart page 6. Discuss what is happening in the photograph by asking:

- **What kind of animal do you see? Name it.** Have a volunteer circle an animal.

- **Where are the animals?** Have a volunteer point to the body of water. Explain that this body of water is called a *pond*. Encourage children to share what they know about ducks and ponds

- **What other animals might you see at a pond?** (Possible answers: frogs, fish, swans, turtles) **What kind of plants might you see by a pond?** (Possible answers: grass, trees, cattails, flowers)

- Explain to children that in this unit, they will learn about animals and plants.

Introduce the Floor Puzzle

- Tell children that they will put together a puzzle that looks just like the photograph on Flip Chart page 6.

- Place the puzzle pieces on the floor and invite children to work as a group to put the puzzle together. Tell them that they can use the photograph on the flip chart to help them. Provide assistance as needed.

- As children are working on the puzzle, ask the following questions:
  Where are the ducks in the photograph?
  What color are the ducks?
  What color is the water in the pond?
  What surrounds the pond?

- Explain to children that the puzzle will be in the Science Center. They will have other opportunities to put the puzzle together again and discuss the picture on the puzzle as they learn more about **Life Science.**

Unit A: Life Science

Materials List for Unit A

Activities	Kit materials	School-supplied materials
How can you use sight and touch to tell about objects? pp. 26–27	rubber ball feather hand lens rocks cotton balls	
What shapes do leaves have? pp. 38–39		masking tape leaves paint paintbrush construction paper
What are animals like? pp. 50–51	animal picture cards	
How can you show different animal homes? pp. 60–61		safety scissors masking tape magazines construction paper crayons

Unit A Bibliography

Teachers may want to share the following books with children to expand their comprehension of science concepts taught in Unit A.

You may wish to place some or all of these books in the Science Center after reading them aloud to children.

A Handful of Sunshine
By Melanie Eclare
[Ragged Bears, Inc., ISBN 1-929927-14-2, 2000]
This book tells how a young gardener grows a sunflower. **Challenge**

Across the Stream
by Mirra Ginsburg
[Greenwillow Books, 1SBN 0-688-10477-0,1982]
This book tells about a hen saving her three chicks from a fox. (Helps identify characteristics of animals and their babies.) **Challenge**

Exactly the Opposite
by Tana Hoban
[Harper, Trophy, ISBN 0-688-15473-5, 1997]
In this wordless book, the photographs show a variety of people, animals, and objects as pairs of opposites. **Challenge**

From Caterpillar to Butterfly
By Deborah Heiligman
[HarperCollins, ISBN 0-06-024268-X, 1996]
This is an easy-to-read science book with helpful illustrations that explain how caterpillars turn to butterflies.

From Tadpole to Frog
by Wendy Pfeffer
[HarperCollins, ISBN 0-06-445123-2,1994]
This is a science book that uses pictures to explain the growth of a frog.

I Took a Walk
by Henry Cole
[Greenwillow Books, ISBN 0-688-15115-9, 11998]
This book tells of a child's walk through the woods and the creatures he sees. (Helps with living things.) **Challenge**

In the Small, Small Pond
by Denise Fleming
[Henry Holt and Company, Inc., ISBN 0-8050-2264-3,1993]
This book tells about animals that make a small pond their home.

Listen...What Do You Hear?
by Nicolas Wood and Jennifer Rye
[Troll Associates, ISBN 0-8167-2121-1, 1991]
This book uses exciting pictures to encourage children to learn about the world around them. **Challenge**

Panda Bear, Panda Bear, What Do You See?
by Bill Martin Jr. and Eric Carle
[Henry Holt and Company, ISBN 0-8050-1758-5, 2003]
This book introduces children to an assortment of unusual animals. **Challenge**

The Very Hungry Caterpillar
by Eric Carle
[Philomel Books, ISBN 0-399-20853-4,1987]
This book tells of a caterpillar's transformation into a butterfly. (Helps with a discussion how animals change as they grow and develop.)

The Yellow Balloon
by Charlotte Dematons
[Front Street/Lemniscaat, ISBN 1-93245-01-2, 2003]
A wordless picture book follows a balloon sailing around the word. (Helps identify living and nonliving things.)

Where Did Bunny Go?
by Nancy Tofuri
[Scholastic Press, ISBN 0-439-16959-3, 2001]
This book tells about a rabbit that hides from its friends. (Helps prompt discussion of an animal's home.) **Challenge**

Unit A: Planning Guide

Lesson/Activity	Pacing	Science Objectives/Vocabulary
Activity How can you use sight and touch to tell about objects? pp. 26–27	15 minutes	Children will identify and describe different objects.
1 What are your five senses? pp. 28–29	20 minutes	Children identify the five senses. hear, taste, touch, smell, see
2 What are living and nonliving things? pp. 30–31	20 minutes	Children will understand that plants, animals, and people are living things. living thing, nonliving thing, plant, animal
3 What do living things need? pp. 32–33	20 minutes	Children will define a need as something a living thing must have to live. air, food, shelter, sunlight, water
4 What do living things do? pp. 34–35	20 minutes	Children will recognize that animals and plants grow and move. grow, move, crawl
Activity What shapes do leaves have? pp. 38–39	15 minutes	Children will recognize that leaves have different shapes.
5 What are some different kinds of plants? pp. 40–41	20 minutes	Children will identify different kinds of plants. bush, grass, tree, vegetable
6 What are the parts of a plant? pp. 42–43	20 minutes	Children will identify the four parts of a plant. flower, stem, leaf, roots

Lesson/Activity	Pacing	Science Objectives/Vocabulary
7 Where do plants live? pp. 44–45	20 minutes	Children will identify different plant habitats. desert, farm, forest, garden
8 How do plants grow? pp. 46–47	20 minutes	Children will identify steps in the life cycle of a plant. fruit, seed, seedling, soil
Activity What are animals like? pp. 50–51	15 minutes	Children will describe different physical characteristics of animals.
9 What can you tell about animals? pp. 52–53	20 minutes	Children will identify characteristics of insects, birds, fish, and reptiles. insect, bird, fish, lizard, wings, fins
10 How do animals move? pp. 54–55	20 minutes	Children will identify different ways that animals move. hop, fly, run, swim
11 How are animals alike and different? pp. 56–57	20 minutes	Children will identify how baby animals and adult animals are alike and different. alike, different
12 Where do animals live? pp. 58–59	20 minutes	Children will identify animal habitats. ocean, land, cold
Activity How can you show different animal homes? pp. 60–61	15 minutes	Children will identify the homes of different animals.
ASSESSMENT pp. 143–146		

Science Songs and Poems

> ## Objective
> Children will:
> - Sing a song to develop oral language.
> - Understand that they can see, hear, taste, smell, and feel to learn about things.
>
> **You need:** Flip Chart page 7, dinosaur puppet

1 Build Background

Begin a discussion about the things children can do such as hear things, see things and so on without using the term senses.

2 What to Do

- Tell children that they will learn a song today. Have children listen as you hum the tune of "My Darling Clementine." Hum a few times and then invite children to hum along with you.

- When children are ready, sing "I'm Alive" to the tune of "My Darling Clementine."
  Sing the verse several times, inviting children to sing with you.

- Direct children's attention to Flip Chart page 7 and have children discuss the picture. Prompt children as needed with questions.

- Then sing the song again using "Annie" the dinosaur puppet.

- Call on volunteers to name things they can smell, feel, see, taste and hear. Accept any reasonable responses.

3 Talk About It

- Point to the word *alive* in the song. Say the word and have children repeat it after you. Tell children that *alive* means "having life" or "living."

- Invite volunteers to complete this sentence: "I'm alive and I can ____." (See, hear, taste, and so on.)

You may also wish to teach children the following poems and finger plays with these lessons.

(Lesson 1)

Use your eyes, use your eyes,
What do you see?
If you have brown eyes
Come and stand by me.

Use your ears, use your ears
What do you hear?
I hear a soft sound
What do you now hear?

Use your nose, use your nose,
What do you smell?
When you think you know
Raise your hand and tell.

(Lessons 2–3)

Once I saw a bunny
(Extend index and middle fingers of one hand apart.)

And a green, green cabbage head.
(Ball other hand into a fist.)

"I think I'll have some cabbage,"
The little bunny said.

So he nibbled and he nibbled,
(Making bobbing motion with first hand.)

And he perked his ears to say,
(Extend index and middle fingers upward.)

"Now I think it's time I should be hopping on my way."
(Let hand hop away.)

(Lesson 4)

There's something about me
That I'm knowing.
There's something about me
That isn't showing.
I'm growing.

How can you use sight and touch to tell about objects?

Objective
Children will:
• Identify and describe different objects.

1 Build Background

This activity helps children think about what they learn from looking at and touching objects.

Managing Time and Materials

Time: 15 minutes
Grouping: whole class

Materials: Flip Chart page 8
pencil, small rubber ball, feather, cotton balls, and a rock or other objects that are soft, hard and have different textures, hand lens

2 What to Do

Engage Display Flip Chart page 8 and read the title to the children. Name the objects pictured. (Rubber ball, feather, pebbles, cotton balls, and hand lens) Ask questions under **Build Background** at the bottom of Flip Chart page 8. Place the objects on a table. Then say: **We will be learning about these objects by looking at them and touching them. First let's <u>look</u> at the objects and name them. If you know the name of each object say it with me as I point to it.** Now point to each object on the chart and say its name.

Explore Invite a child to come up to the chart. Tell the child to look at the object first, without touching the picture. Say: **<u>Tell</u> us about the object.** Encourage the child to describe the object by color, size, and shape. Repeat children's answers using complete sentences. For example, if a child says that an object is red, then you say: **The (Object) is red.** Have children repeat the sentence after you.

Then ask the child to **touch** the same object on the table. **What else can you tell us about the object? What else did you learn about _____ by touching it? Why?** Repeat children's answers using complete sentences. Prompt children to repeat each complete sentence after you. Continue in this manner with each object and other volunteers.

Explain Guide children in talking about each object and explain how we use the object in our everyday lives. Encourage children to tell where they have seen this object, how it is used, and how it feels to the touch.

Evaluate Have children tell how objects are alike and different. Ask: **How are the rock and the cotton balls different? How are the cotton balls and the ball alike? How are they different?** Repeat children's answers using complete sentences. Then have children repeat the sentences after you.

Extend Do the same activity again using the hand lens. Encourage children to tell how different the object looks now!

3 Discuss the Results

1. **Observe** What can you learn about an object when you look at it and touch it? (Answers may include color, size, shape, and texture.)

2. **Classify** Name other objects that are soft to the touch. (Possible answers: Pillow, cloth, sweater, towel)

Go Further Think of the rule: Stop, listen, and look. Which parts of your body do you use when you look and listen? (Eyes and ears) Repeat children's answers using complete sentences. Prompt children to repeat the sentences after you.

Process Skills

Tell children that they can make **observations** when they find out about things. Explain that when they talk about each object, they are also **communicating** their ideas and opinions.

Listening and Speaking Tip

• Remind children to listen politely when others are called upon to speak. They should not interrupt a speaker. Explain that children must wait for their turn to answer a question.

What are your five senses?

> ## Objectives
> Children will:
> • Identify the five senses.
> • Tell how each sense helps them learn about living and nonliving things.
>
> **You need:** Flip Chart pages 7, 9, dinosaur puppet

Build Background

Pantomime each vocabulary word. Ask children what you are doing. Ask what you may have learned by listening, tasting, touching, smelling, and seeing.

Circle Time!

Sing "I'm Alive"

• Bring children to the circle by singing "I'm Alive" on Flip Chart page 7.

• As children come to the circle and sit, track the words on the chart with your finger and encourage children to sing along. Use the dinosaur puppet to sing the song again once everyone is sitting.

Talk About It!

• Use Flip Chart page 9 to review vocabulary terms before you begin to teach Lesson 1.

• Guide **oral vocabulary** development by asking the following questions: **What does the girl use to hear the puppy bark?** (Ears) **What does the girl use to see the puppy?** (Eyes) **What does the girl use to find out how the puppy feels?** (Sense of touch) **What does the girl use to smell?** (Nose)

Learn About It!

• Use Teacher Instructions at the bottom of Flip Chart page 9 to guide science lesson. Children should understand that they have five senses: hearing, seeing, touching, tasting, and smelling. Senses help them to find out about the world around them.

• Have children use the picture clues and answer the questions. Expand on children's responses by using them in complete sentences. Prompt children to repeat the sentences.

• Call on volunteers to circle the appropriate pictures.

Vocabulary

hear: receiving sound through the ears

taste: the flavor of something

touch: using your hands to feel something

smell: using the nose to notice an odor

see: using eyes to notice things or people

- Continue questioning by asking the following: **What can you learn about things you see?** (You can learn how things look.) **What can you learn about things you taste?** (You can learn about the foods you eat.)

- Have children explain their answer for the **Draw Conclusions** question. (Taste, smell)

Differentiate Instruction

Full Day or Extended Instruction

- Hold up pictures showing people using their senses to taste, touch, smell, see, or hear things.

- Call on children, in turn, to talk about each picture using the appropriate "sense" word.

Reteaching and English Language Learner Support

- Revisit the terms *hear, taste, touch, see, smell* by showing children a picture of each word. Help children identify each picture.

- Encourage children to summarize what they know about each sense by using complete sentences. Model sentences for them as necessary. "I use my eyes to ___. I use my hands to ___. I use my mouth to ___."

Monitor Progress

Monitor Progress

- Use "Talk About It," "Learn About It," and Centers activities to check children's progress through the week.

- Refer to "Differentiate Instruction" for reteaching tips.

- Use Assessment Sheet on Teacher's Edition page 143 to record each child's understanding of concepts covered in this lesson.

Science Centers

Center 1: Science Song "I'm Alive"

Play "I'm Alive" for the children in the listening center. Encourage children to sing along. Provide each child with a copy of the song to track words, illustrate, and take home to share, as appropriate.

Center 2: Cross-Curricular Link

Math Ask children to count the number of blue objects they see in the center. Ask children to count the number of square objects they see in the center. Have children dictate their answers in complete sentences as you record their responses on strips of paper.

Center 3: Science Journal

Ask children to draw a picture of something they would like to taste or smell in their **Discovery Journal**. Have children dictate a word or a sentence about their picture.

Lesson 2

What are living and nonliving things?

Objectives

Children will:
- Understand that living things are plants, animals, and people.
- Understand that nonliving things are common objects we see every day.
- Discover the difference between living and nonliving things.

You need: Flip Chart pages 7, 10; pictures of living and nonliving things, dinosaur puppet

Build Background

Display two pictures, one of a living thing (A person or an animal) and one of a nonliving thing (Object). Hold up both pictures and have children identify the picture that shows a living thing.

Circle Time!

Sing "I'm Alive"
- Bring children to the circle by singing "I'm Alive" on Flip Chart page 7.
- As children come to the circle and sit, track the words on the chart with your finger and encourage children to sing along. Sing the song again once everyone is sitting.

Talk About It!

- Use Flip Chart page 10 to review vocabulary terms before you begin to teach Lesson 2.

- Guide **oral vocabulary** development by asking the following questions: **What is something in the picture that is alive, or living?** (Girl, fish, plant) **What is something that is not alive, or nonliving?** (Accept any object shown in picture.) **What is the girl doing in the picture?** (She is feeding the fish.) Remind children to answer using complete sentences.

Learn About It!

- Use **Teacher Instructions** at bottom of flip chart page 10 to guide science lesson. Children should understand that nonliving things cannot move, grow or change on their own. Living things can move, grow, and change. Help children realize that plants, animals, and people are living things.

Vocabulary

living thing: something that is alive; living things grow, move and change.

nonliving thing: something that is not alive; nonliving things do not grow.

plant: is a living thing; a plant grows in one place.

animal: is a living thing; an animal grows, moves about, and changes.

- Have children use the picture clues and answer the questions. Expand on children's responses by using them in complete sentences. Prompt children to repeat the sentences.

- Call on volunteers to circle and put an X on the appropriate pictures.

- Continue questioning by asking the following: **Why is the chair nonliving?** [Possible answer: It cannot move, grow, or change.] **Why is the fish a living thing?** [Possible answer: It can move, eat, and grow.]

- Have children share their answer to the **Compare/Contrast** question. (They are living things.)

Differentiate Instruction

Full Day or Extended Instruction

- Assign a group of children to find living things in the classroom. Assign another group to find nonliving things. Place as many items as possible on a table.

- Then call on children, in turn, to name a living or nonliving thing that they found in the room and explain their choice.

- Help children talk about what they know about why something is living or nonliving.

Reteaching and English Language Learner Support

- Revisit the terms *nonliving, living, animal,* and *plant* by showing children a picture of each word. Help children identify each picture.

- Encourage children to tell what they know about living and nonliving things by using complete sentences. Model sentences for them as necessary.

Science Centers

Center 1: Science Song "I'm Alive"

Play "I'm Alive" for the children in the listening center. Encourage children to sing along. Provide each child with a copy of the song to track words, illustrate, and take home to share, as appropriate. Children may enjoy taking turns using the dinosaur puppet as they sing along.

Center 2: Cross-Curricular Link

Language Arts: Display a large picture/poster that shows many living things. Have children work in pairs and name the living things. Encourage children to talk about each living thing by saying: "This _____ is a living thing."

Center 3: Science Journal

Ask children to draw a picture of a living thing in their **Discovery Journal.** Have children dictate a word or a sentence about their picture.

Monitor Progress
- Use "Talk About It," "Learn About It," and Centers activities to check children's progress through the week.
- Refer to "Differentiate Instruction" for reteaching tips.
- Use Assessment Sheet on Teacher's Edition page 143 to record each child's understanding of concepts covered in this lesson.

Lesson 3

What do living things need?

Objectives

Children will:
- Define a need as something a living thing must have.
- Identify that all living things need food, air, and water to live.

You need: Flip Chart pages 7, 11

Build Background

Display a plant and a block. Alternatively, you can use pictures of a living and a nonliving thing. Ask children to tell which thing is living. Explain that in this lesson, they will learn about what living things need to stay alive.

Circle Time!

Sing "I'm Alive"

- Bring children to the circle by singing "I'm Alive" on Flip Chart page 7.

- As children come to the circle and sit, track the words on the chart with your finger and encourage children to sing along. Sing the song again once everyone is sitting.

Vocabulary

air: mixture of gases around Earth

food: anything that living things take in to keep them alive

shelter: a safe place that protects or covers

sunlight: light from the Sun

water: liquid that falls from the sky as rain and found in oceans, rivers, and lakes

Talk About It!

- Use Flip Chart page 11 to review vocabulary terms before you begin to teach Lesson 3.

- Guide **oral vocabulary** development by asking the following questions: **What kind of living things do you see in the picture?** (Girl, plants, bird) **What is the girl drinking?** (Water) **What are the girl and the bird breathing?** (Air) **What is falling on the flowers?** (Water)

Learn About It!

- Use **Teacher Instructions** at the bottom of Flip Chart page 11 to guide the science lesson. Children should understand that people and animals need air, water, food, and shelter to stay alive. Plants need air, water, food, and sunshine to live.

- Have children use the picture clues and answer the questions. Expand on children's responses by using them in complete sentences. Prompt children to repeat the sentences.

- Call on volunteers to circle and put an X on the appropriate pictures.

- Continue questioning by asking the following: **Why do people and animals need shelter?** (Possible answer: Shelter protects them from the weather.) **Where do plants get the water they need?** (Possible answer: Most water comes from rain. People also water plants.)

- Have children explain their answer for the **Infer** question. (To keep them alive)

Differentiate Instruction

Full Day or Extended Instruction

- Divide children into five groups and assign each group one of these needs: air, food, shelter, sunlight, water. Distribute old magazines and scissors to each group. Help each group cut out a picture showing a living thing getting this need.

- Have each group hold up their picture and talk about the living thing and needs.

Reteaching and English Language Learner Support

- Revisit the terms *air, food, shelter, sunlight,* and *water* by showing children a picture of each word. Help children identify each picture.

- Encourage children to summarize what animals and people need to stay alive. Then have them tell what plants need to live. Encourage them to use complete sentences and provide models for them as necessary.

Monitor Progress

- Use "Talk About It," "Learn About It," and Centers activities to check children's progress through the week.

- Refer to "Differentiate Instruction" for reteaching tips.

- Use Assessment Sheet on Teacher's Edition page 143 to record each child's understanding of concepts covered in this lesson.

Science Centers

Center 1: Science Song "I'm Alive"

Play "I'm Alive" for the children in the listening center. Encourage children to sing along. Provide each child with a copy of the song to track words, illustrate, and take home to share, as appropriate.

Center 2: Cross-Curricular Link

Art Distribute craft sticks and modeling clay to each child. Have children make a home for an animal. Call on volunteers to show and tell about their animal home.

Center 3: Science Journal

Ask children to draw pictures of a pet they have or would like to have in their **Discovery Journal**. In their picture, have them show how they are helping this pet meet one of its needs. Have children dictate a word or a sentence about their picture.

Lesson 4

What do living things do?

Objectives

Children will:
- Recognize that animals and people can grow and move.
- Recognize that plants can grow.

You need: Flip Chart pages 7, 12

Build Background

Display a baby's jacket or sweater. Ask children if they could wear it now and tell why or why not. Guide them to understand that it would not fit because their bodies have grown and changed since they were babies.

Circle Time!

Sing "I'm Alive"

- Bring children to the circle by singing "I'm Alive" on Flip Chart page 7.

- As children come to the circle and sit, track the words on the chart with your finger and encourage children to sing along. Sing the song again once everyone is sitting.

Vocabulary

grow: to become bigger

move: to change position or place

crawl: to move very slowly

Talk About It!

- Use Flip Chart page 12 to review vocabulary terms before you begin to teach Lesson 4.

- Guide **oral vocabulary** development by asking the following questions: **What can the baby do?** (Crawl, smile, laugh, and so on) **About how old do you think the boy is?** (Four, five) **What is he doing?** (Walking) **Which of the two plants is probably older? What makes you think this?** (The yellow sunflower because it's bigger)

Learn About It!

- Use **Teacher Instructions** at the bottom of Flip Chart page 12 to guide the science lesson. Children should understand that all living things grow and change over time. People and animals are also able to move from one place to another while plants usually stay in one place.

- Have children use the picture clues and answer the questions. Expand on children's responses by using them in complete sentences. Prompt children to repeat the sentences.

Science Misconception

Size Is Not Always an Indicator of Age

Children may think that a person's size indicates his or her age. Explain that people grow at different speeds, and that some people grow taller than others.

Listening and Speaking Tip

Respectful Listening

• Tell children that it is important for everyone to have an opportunity to share his or her ideas. Remind them to listen carefully and not to talk when others speak. Suggest that they wait to ask questions until the speaker is finished talking.

Monitor Progress

• Use "Talk About It," "Learn About It," and Centers activities to check children's progress through the week.

• Refer to "Differentiate Instruction" for reteaching tips.

• Use Assessment Sheet on Teacher's Edition page 143 to record each child's understanding of concepts covered in this lesson.

• Call on volunteers to circle and put an X on the appropriate pictures.

• Continue questioning by asking the following: **How will the boy grow as he gets older?** (Possible answer: He will grow taller. He will be able to do many more things.) **What other kinds of living things can move?** (Possible answer: Animals can move.)

• Have children explain their answer for the **Compare** question. (Grow)

Differentiate Instruction

Full Day or Extended Instruction

• Ask children to bring in photographs of themselves when they were babies or toddlers. If children cannot bring in photos, ask them to draw themselves as babies.

• Invite children to share their photographs or pictures with the group. **How have you changed since you were a baby? What are you able to do now that you could not do when you were a baby?**

• Then invite children to think about ways they will change as they grow older. **How do you think you will look then? What do you think you will be able to do when you are older?**

Reteaching and English Language Learner Support

• Revisit the terms *grow* and *move*. Have children use their hands to show how something grows.

• Ask children to summarize what living things do. Ask them to tell what is different about what people and plants can do.

Science Centers

Center 1: Science Song "I'm Alive"

Play "I'm Alive" for the children in the listening center. Encourage children to sing along. Provide each child with a copy of the song to track words, illustrate, and take home to share, as appropriate.

Center 2: Cross-Curricular Link

Drama Display a picture of an egg and explain that there is a baby duck inside that is almost ready to break through the shell. Have children pantomime the duckling breaking through the shell and trying to move. Then have them act out how the duckling will change and grow over time.

Center 3: Science Journal

Ask children to draw a picture showing how they will grow and change as an adult in their **Discovery Journal**. In their picture, have them show something that they will be able to do that they cannot do now. Have children dictate a word or a sentence about their picture.

Science Songs and Poems

> ## Objective
> Children will:
> - Sing a song to develop oral language.
> - Distinguish between living and nonliving things.
>
> **You need:** Flip Chart page 13, dinosaur puppet

1 Build Background

Begin a discussion about living things by asking children to identify living things (Animals and plants). Ask what living things need and what living things do.

2 What to Do

- Tell children that they will learn a song today. Have children listen as you hum the tune of "Cockles and Mussels." Hum a few times and then invite children to hum along with you.

- When children are ready, sing "Plants" to the tune of "Cockles and Mussels." Sing the verse several times, inviting children to sing with you.

- Direct children's attention to Flip Chart page 13 and have children discuss the picture. Prompt children as needed with questions.

- Then sing the song again using "Annie" the dinosaur puppet.

- Call on volunteers to discuss why they think a plant is a living thing. (It grows.)

3 Talk About It

- Point to the word *ground* in the song. Say the word and have children repeat it after you. Tell children that *ground* is another word for *soil* or *land*.

- Invite volunteers to complete this sentence: "I see a _____ in the ground."

You may also wish to teach children the following poems and finger plays with these lessons.

(Lesson 5)

My Garden

This is my garden;
(Extend one hand forward, palm up.)

I'll rake it with care.
(Make raking motion on palm with fingers of opposite hand.)

And then some flower seeds

I'll plant there.
(Make circle with hand.)

The sun will shine.
(Make circle with hands.)

The rain will fall.
(Let fingers flutter down to lap.)

My garden will blossom,
(Cup hands together and slowly extend upward.)

And grow straight and tall.
(Stand tall with arms overhead.)

(Lesson 6)

A Plant

Here's a leaf,
(Show hand.)

And here's a stem,
(Raise pointer finger.)

And here's a flower, too.
(Open cupped hands.)

Underground there are some roots,
(Wiggle fingers.)

Hidden from your view.

(Lesson 8)

Gardening

Dig! Dig! Dig! Rake just so.
Plant the seeds; watch them grow.
Chop! Chop! Chop! Pull out seeds.
Warm rain and sun, my garden needs.
Up! Up! Up! Green stems climb.
Open wide; it's blossom time.

Activity

What shapes do leaves have?

> ## Objective
> Children will:
> • Recognize that leaves have different shapes.
> • Recognize that leaves are plant parts.

1 Build Background

This activity helps children to observe and describe leaves with different shapes.

Managing Time and Materials

Time: 15 minutes
Grouping: whole class

Materials: Flip Chart page 14
leaves, tape, drawing paper, paintbrush, paint

2 What to Do

Engage Display Flip Chart page 14. Read aloud the title as you track the text. Help children identify the pictured materials. (Leaves, tape, paper, paintbrush, and paint) Say: **Look at the flip chart. Use your finger to trace its shape in the air. What other things in this room have the same shape as this page?** If necessary, guide children to mention other rectangular shapes, such as a sheet of paper, a door, a window, or a poster. Say: **Shapes like this are called rectangles.** Then display a penny. **What objects can you name that have the same shape as a penny?** Have children use a finger to trace a penny's shape in the air. **What do we call this shape?** (Circle) Tell children they will learn more about the shapes of leaves.

Explore Tell children that making leaf prints can help them see leaf shapes more clearly. Work with children to help them make leaf prints. Begin by having volunteers **tape** several leaves on a sheet of paper. Then have others **paint** the leaves with a thin coat of paint. Carefully place a second sheet of paper directly on top of the leaves; then call on several other volunteers to gently rub the paper over the leaves. Finally, have a volunteer help you carefully remove the paper to display the prints. Say: **Look at the leaf prints. Tell what you observe. What shapes do these leaf prints have?**

Explain Guide children in describing their observations. As you ask the following questions, have children point to specific leaf prints to illustrate their answers. Ask: **Which of the leaves have a round shape? Which look like a triangle? Which of the leaves are long and thin? Which are short and wide? Which are small, and which are large? Do any of the leaves have a smooth edge? Are there some with jagged edges?**

Evaluate Invite children to tell where the leaves they used to make leaf prints came from. Ask: **What is the same about all leaves?** (All leaves come from plants.) Have children finger trace several leaf shapes in the air. **What differences do you notice in leaves?** (Leaves come in many different shapes and sizes.)

Extend Provide other leaves, duplicating paper, and peeled crayons. Then model how to make a leaf rubbing by placing a leaf under a sheet of duplicating paper and rubbing over it with the side of a peeled crayon. Invite children to describe what the rubbing reveals. Explain that the small "branches" that they observe on the leaves are called "veins." Then have children describe the shapes of these leaves.

3 Discuss the Results

Listening and Speaking Tip

• Encourage children to look people in the eyes when speaking. Explain that this is called "making eye contact." Tell them that when they are listening to others speak, they should look at the speaker and smile or nod their head to show that they are listening.

1. **Observe** What leaf shapes did you observe when you made leaf prints? (Possible answer: Leaves can be round or like triangles. Some leaves are wide and others are long and thin. Leaves have different kinds of edges.)

2. **Generalize** Why do you think these leaves have such different shapes? (Possible answer: These leaves come from different kinds of plants, and so the leaves look different.)

Go Further Provide children with other natural objects such as shells, flat pebbles, and small pieces of driftwood. Have children press these objects into soft clay or play dough to create molds. Encourage them to observe the shapes and textures of the objects by asking: **What does the mold you made show?** (The shape and size of the object) Point out roughness or smoothness of the object can also be observed in the clay.

Process Skills

Tell children that they are **collecting data** about leaves when they help to make leaf prints. Point out that they are **communicating** when they share their observations about leaf shapes in conversations with their classmates.

What are some different kinds of plants?

Objectives

Children will:

• Identify different kinds of plants.

• Recall that plants need air, water, sunshine, and space to grow.

You need: Flip Chart pages 13, 15

Build Background

Display pictures of a healthy plant and a plant that is not getting what it needs to grow. Ask children to recall what living things need. Then have them identify the plant that looks like it is getting what it needs.

Circle Time!

Sing "Plants"

• Bring children to the circle by singing "Plants" on Flip Chart page 13.

• As children come to the circle and sit, track the words on the chart with your finger and encourage children to sing along. Sing the song again once everyone is sitting.

Talk About It!

• Use Flip Chart page 15 to review vocabulary terms before you begin to teach Lesson 5.

• Guide **oral vocabulary** development by asking the following questions: **What kind of plants do you recognize? Which is larger—the tree or the bush?** (Tree) **Where does grass grow?** (In the park) **How are the plants getting the water they need?** (Through a sprinkler) **Which of these plants would you find in a garden?** (Vegetables) Remind children to answer using complete sentences.

Learn About It!

• Use **Teacher Instructions** at the bottom of Flip Chart page 15 to guide the science lesson. Children should understand that there are different kinds of plants; however, all plants need water, air, sunshine, food, and space to grow.

• Have children use the picture clues and answer the questions. Expand on children's responses by using them in complete sentences. Prompt children to repeat the sentences.

Vocabulary

bush: a woody plant smaller than a tree

grass: plants with narrow green leaves that cover lawns and pastures

tree: a large plant with a woody trunk usually having branches and leaves

vegetable: a plant whose roots, stems, leaves, seeds, or pods are sometimes used for food

- Continue questioning by asking the following: **In what ways are trees and bushes different?** (Possible answer: Most trees grow larger than bushes. Usually bushes are covered all over with branches.)
- Have children explain their answer for the **Infer** question. (Vegetables)

Differentiate Instruction

Full Day or Extended Instruction
- Take children on a walk on school grounds or in the community to look for different kinds of plants. Guide them to see examples of trees, bushes, grass, vegetables, and flowers.
- Upon your return to the classroom, hang up mural paper and provide children with crayons, markers, or paints and brushes. Invite them to create a classroom garden in which they show a variety of plants. Have children dictate labels or captions for some of the plants.

Reteaching and English Language Learner Support
- Reinforce the words *bush, grass, tree,* and *vegetable* by showing children a picture of each word. After children identify the plant, ask them simple yes/no questions about it.
- Direct children's attention to Flip Chart page 12 again. Play an "I Spy" game in which you give clues about the illustration. **Can you spy something that gives plants water?**

Science Centers

Center 1: Science Song "Plants"
Play "Plants" for the children in the listening center. Encourage children to sing along. Provide each child with a copy of the song to track words, illustrate, and take home to share, as appropriate.

Center 2: Cross-Curricular Link
Social Studies Display samples of various grains, such as rice, millet, oats, barley, and buckwheat. Explain that these grains are types of grasses that grow in different parts of the world. Point out that they may be cooked and eaten as is or they may be prepared as parts of other food, such as bread, crackers, cereal, porridge, or soup. After checking for food allergies, provide children with small samples of rice, oat, and wheat crackers on paper towels. Invite those who wish to taste these samples and describe their flavors.

Center 3: Science Journal
Ask children to draw pictures showing something they could do to make sure that a classroom plant gets what it needs to live. Have children dictate a word or a sentence about their picture.

Monitor Progress
- Use "Talk About It," "Learn About It," and Centers activities to check children's progress through the week.
- Refer to "Differentiate Instruction" for reteaching tips.
- Use Assessment Sheet on Teacher's Edition page 144 to record each child's understanding of concepts covered in this lesson.

Lesson 6

What are the parts of a plant?

Objectives

Children will:
• Identify the four main parts of a plant.

You need: Flip Chart pages 13, 16

Build Background

Display a picture of a plant. Then have children tell what they know about plants. Encourage them to name any parts of the plant that they recognize.

Circle Time!

Sing "Plants"

• Bring children to the circle by singing "Plants" on Flip Chart page 13.

• As children come to the circle and sit, track the words on the chart with your finger and encourage children to sing along. Sing the song again once everyone is sitting.

Vocabulary

flower: a part of a plant that makes seeds

leaf: one of the thin, flat green parts of a tree or other plant

roots: the part of the plant that grows underground

stem: the part of the plant that supports leaves and flowers

Talk About It!

• Use Flip Chart page 16 to review vocabulary terms before you begin to teach Lesson 6.

• Guide **oral vocabulary** development by asking the following questions: **What part of the plant holds up the flowers?** (Stem) **What other plant parts are attached to the stems of this plant?** (Leaf, flower) **Which part of this plant grows in the soil?** (Roots) Remind children to answer using complete sentences.

Learn About It!

• Use **Teacher Instructions** at the bottom of Flip Chart page 16 to guide the science lesson. Children should understand that most plants have four main parts: leaf, roots, stem, and flowers.

• Have children use the picture clues and answer the questions. Expand on children's responses by using them in complete sentences. Prompt children to repeat the sentences.

• Call on volunteers to circle and put an X on the appropriate pictures.

Science Misconception

How Plants Get Food

Children may think that plants get most of their food from the soil. Explain to children that plants make their own food. When light shines on the leaves, special parts of the leaves, called chloroplasts, take in energy from the light. Chloroplasts are found in cells. The plants use this energy to make their own food.

- Continue questioning by asking the following: **How are the parts of this plant like the parts of a tree?** (Possible answer: Both this plant and trees have leaves and roots. The stem of a plant is thinner than the trunk of a tree. This plant has flowers and so do some trees.)

- Have children explain their answer for the **Classify** question. (Roots)

Differentiate Instruction

Full Day or Extended Instruction

- Help children examine potted plants by gently removing one from a pot and carefully brushing away part of the soil so that children can observe the roots. Guide them to observe that the root is thicker where it connects to the stem and then branches out into smaller rootlets.

- Discuss the parts of the plant that grow above ground. Point out that the stem holds up the leaves, flowers.

Reteaching and English Language Learner Support

- Reinforce the words *flower*, *leaf*, *roots*, and *stem* by displaying a potted plant and having children point to the relevant plant part as you name each one.

Science Centers

Center 1: Science Song "Plants"

Play "Plants" for the children in the listening center. Encourage children to sing along. Provide each child with a copy of the song to track words, illustrate, and take home to share, as appropriate.

Center 2: Cross-Curricular Link

Language Arts Display three potted plants or pictures of different plants. Make sure that the foliage is a different shape or color, the height of the stems is different, and that the plants have flowers that are a different size, shape, or color. Then have children take turns choosing one of the plants and describing its size, shape, or color.

Center 3: Science Journal

Ask children to draw a picture of a plant showing its parts. Encourage them to look at Flip Chart 16 for guidance. Have children identify each part. Label the part as it is identified.

Monitor Progress

- Use "Talk About It," "Learn About It," and Centers activities to check children's progress through the week.

- Refer to "Differentiate Instruction" for reteaching tips.

- Use Assessment Sheet on Teacher's Edition page 144 to record each child's understanding of concepts covered in this lesson.

Lesson 7

Where do plants live?

Objectives

Children will:
• Identify different plant habitats.

You need: Flip Chart pages 13, 17

Build Background

Remind children that they have been learning about plants. Ask them to recall places where they have seen plants growing. Encourage them to think of places in their home, in school, and in the neighborhood.

Circle Time!

Sing "Plants"

• Bring children to the circle by singing "Plants" on Flip Chart page 13.

• As children come to the circle and sit, track the words on the chart with your finger and encourage children to sing along. Sing the song again once everyone is sitting.

Vocabulary

desert: a dry sandy region without water or trees

farm: a place where food crops and animals are raised

forest: a large area with many trees, plants, and animals

garden: a piece of land where flowers or vegetables are grown

Talk About It!

• Use Flip Chart page 17 to review vocabulary terms before you begin to teach Lesson 7.

• Guide **oral vocabulary** development by asking the following questions: **What kinds of plants grow on farms?** (Vegetables, grain, and so on) **What do you call a place where trees grow very close together?** (Forest) **Which picture shows a place where it is very dry and hardly ever rains? What do you call this place?** (Desert) **What do you call a place where people grow plants in their yards?** (Garden) Remind children to answer using complete sentences.

Learn About It!

• Use **Teacher Instructions** at the bottom of Flip Chart page 17 to guide the science lesson. Children should understand that plants grow in many different places. Each of these places has different characteristics.

• Have children use the picture clues and answer the questions. Expand on children's responses by using them in complete sentences. Prompt children to repeat the sentences.

• Call on volunteers to circle and put an X on the appropriate pictures.

• Continue questioning by asking the following: **Could a plant that needs a lot of water grow in a desert? Why?** (Possible answer: No because a desert

Desert Plants

Desert plants have adapted to their dry environment. Most desert cacti have stems that can hold water. They also have long root systems that stay near the surface of the ground. This allows them to absorb water from rainfall as it seeps into the ground.

is a place that gets very little rainfall.) **How might farms and gardens be alike?** (Possible answer: In both places, plants that are used for food are planted and cared for by people.)

• Have children explain their answer for the **Infer** question. (Plants can grow where there is soil, sunlight, and some water.)

Differentiate Instruction

Full Day or Extended Instruction

• Have children work at the sand table or provide a tub of sand and a tub of potting soil. Provide them with construction paper, crayons, scissors, clay or play dough, and plastic animals.

• Divide children into two groups. Tell one group that they will work together to create a model of a desert while the other group works together to model a forest.

• Have them begin by shaping the sand or soil so it resembles desert or forest land. Then have them create plants using construction paper and crayons. Suggest that they add animals that might be found in this place. They can either select from an assortment of plastic animals or model their own from clay or modeling dough.

• When children complete their models, have them describe each place and tell what kind of plants grow there.

Reteaching and English Language Learner Support

• Reinforce the words *desert, farm, forest,* and *garden* by displaying a picture of each place and having children identify it.

• Encourage children to summarize what they know about where different plants grow by using complete sentences. Model sentences for them as necessary. "Plants can grow in a _____ where it is hot and dry." "Plants can grow in a _____ where there are a lot of trees."

Science Centers

Monitor Progress

• Use "Talk About It," "Learn About It," and Centers activities to check children's progress through the week.

• Refer to "Differentiate Instruction" for reteaching tips.

• Use Assessment Sheet on Teacher's Edition page 144 to record each child's understanding of concepts covered in this lesson.

Center 1: Science Song "Plants"

Play "Plants" for the children in the listening center. Encourage children to sing along. Provide each child with a copy of the song to track words, illustrate, and take home to share, as appropriate.

Center 2: Cross-Curricular Link

Writing Display labeled pictures of a desert, a farm, a forest, and a garden. Then provide children with plastic or large die-cut letters. Have them select one of the pictures and identify the place. Then have them use the letters to form the name of the place. Guide children by pointing to each letter and naming it.

Center 3: Science Journal

Ask children to draw a place they would like to visit. Have them show plants that would be found in this place. Have children dictate a word or a sentence about their picture.

Lesson 8

How do plants grow?

Objectives

Children will:

• Identify steps in the life cycle of a plant.

You need: Flip Chart pages 13, 18

Build Background

Remind children that they learned that plants grow. Invite children to imagine that they had a garden. Have them tell what they would do to help the plants grow in their garden.

Circle Time!

Sing "Plants"

• Bring children to the circle by singing "Plants" on Flip Chart page 13.

• As children come to the circle and sit, track the words on the chart with your finger and encourage children to sing along. Sing the song again once everyone is sitting.

Vocabulary

fruit: the part of a plant where seeds are

seed: the part of a plant that grows into a new plant

seedling: a young plant grown from a seed

soil: dirt, the loose top layer of the earth

Talk About It!

• Use Flip Chart page 18 to review vocabulary terms before you begin to teach Lesson 8.

• Guide **oral vocabulary** development by asking the following questions: **Which picture shows a seed? Where would you put this seed so it will grow?** (In soil) **What does the seed turn into once it begins to grow?** (Seedling) **Why do you think this plant is called a seedling? How does the plant change when it is fully grown? In addition to leaves, what else appears on the vine? If you cut open this ripe pumpkin, what do you think you would find inside?** (Seeds) Remind children to answer using complete sentences.

Learn About It!

• Use **Teacher Instructions** at the bottom of Flip Chart page 18 to guide the science lesson. Children should understand that plants follow a cycle of development. Many plants develop from seeds, grow into seedlings, grow flowers, and produce fruit.

• Have children use the picture clues and answer the questions. Expand on children's responses by using them in complete sentences. Prompt children to repeat the sentences.

- Call on volunteers to point to the pictures in order to show how a plant grows.

- Continue questioning by asking the following: **If you kept a pumpkin seed in your pocket, would it grow into a seedling? Why?** (Possible answer: No because a seed needs soil and water to sprout and grow into a seedling.)

- Have children explain their answer for the **Infer** question. (Sunlight, air, water)

Differentiate Instruction

Full Day or Extended Instruction

- Provide children with various types of fruit. Remove the seeds, wash and dry them, and have children examine them using a hand lens.

- Have the class work together to sort the seeds into different groups. They may wish to sort by the size of the seed, by the number of seeds contained in each fruit, by the color of the seeds, or by their texture.

- Have children save several of each type of seed. Then have them plant the seeds in potting soil, keep them moist, and place them in indirect light.

Reteaching and English Language Learner Support

- Reinforce the words *seed, seedling, fruit,* and *soil* by displaying a picture of each object. Help children identify each picture.

- Have children point to each picture on Flip Chart page 18 as they summarize the lifecycle of a pumpkin plant. Encourage them to tell how the plant grows and changes during each stage of its life.

Science Centers

Center 1: Science Song "Plants"

Play "Plants" for the children in the listening center. Encourage children to sing along. Provide each child with a copy of the song to track words, illustrate, and take home to share, as appropriate.

Center 2: Cross-Curricular Link

Art Display dried varieties of peas, beans, lentils, sunflower, and pumpkin seeds. Explain that these are plant seeds that we use as food, and they also are sometimes used by artists to create a special kind of art called a mosaic. Provide children with small squares of cardboard and white glue. Show them how to draw designs with the glue and then fill the area with dried peas, beans, or lentils. To help the seeds stick, have them gently press them in place with their fingers. Once the mosaics are dry, display them on a table or bulletin board under the heading "Seed Art."

Center 3: Science Journal

Ask children to draw a series of pictures, in correct order, showing the growth of a plant, using Flip Chart page 18 as a guide.

Monitor Progress

- Use "Talk About It," "Learn About It," and Centers activities to check children's progress through the week.

- Refer to "Differentiate Instruction" for reteaching tips.

- Use Assessment Sheet on Teacher's Edition page 144 to record each child's understanding of concepts covered in this lesson.

Science Songs and Poems

> ## Objective
> Children will:
> - Sing a song to develop oral language.
> - Recognize that animals are living things.
>
> **You need:** Flip Chart page 19, dinosaur puppet

1 Build Background

Begin a discussion about living things by asking children why a plant is a living thing. (It needs air and water to live. It grows.) Have children explain why they think animals are living things.

2 What to Do

- Tell children that they will learn a song today. Have children listen as you hum the tune of "Rock-A-Bye-Baby." Hum a few times and then invite children to hum along with you.

- When children are ready, sing "Look at the Horse and the Eagle" to the tune of "Rock-A-Bye-Baby." Sing the verse several times, inviting children to sing with you.

- Direct children's attention to Flip Chart page 19 and have children discuss the picture. Prompt children as needed with questions.

- Then sing the song again using "Annie" the dinosaur puppet.

- Discuss the song by asking children how the horse and the eagle are the same. (They are animals. They have legs.) Then ask how the animals are different. (The eagle flies; the horse runs, etc.) Invite children to name other animals that fly; run.

3 Talk About It

- Point to the word *eagle* in the song. Say the word and have children repeat it after you. Tell children that an *eagle* is a large powerful bird.

- Invite volunteers to complete this sentence: "The eagle can ____."
  (Accept any reasonable responses.)

You may also wish to teach children the following poems and finger plays with these lessons.

(Lesson 9)

Let's hear it for the birds,
With feathers so bright.
And don't forget the fish,
With fins on left and right.
Let's cheer for the insects,
With six legs to get around.
As well as scaly lizards,
That crawl across the ground.
These animals are wonderful,
Each in their own way.
Animals! Animals!
Hooray! Hooray!

(Lesson 10)

Frogs jump. Caterpillars hump.
Worms wiggle. Bugs jiggle.
Rabbits hop. Horses clop.
Snakes slide. Seagulls glide.
Mice creep. Deer leap.
Puppies bounce. Kittens pounce.
Lions stalk—but I walk!

(Lesson 11)

Cats have baby kittens.
Their fur is soft as silk.
Dogs have cuddly puppies.
They drink lots of milk.
Hens have downy chicks.
They hatch from eggs, you see.
Bears have furry cubs,
As cute as they can be!

(Lesson 12)

What animals will you see
if you visit a park?
Toads, squirrels, and moths,
And dogs that bark.
What animals will you see
if you visit a beach?
Fish, lobsters, and crabs
with claws that can reach.
What animals will you see
if you visit a farm?
Horses, cows, and pigs,
And sheep in the barn.

What are animals like?

Objective

Children will:
• Describe different physical characteristics.of animals.

1 Build Background

This activity helps children determine how animals are alike and different in their physical characteristics.

Managing Time and Materials

Time: 15 minutes
Grouping: small groups

Materials: Flip Chart page 20 assorted picture cards of animals with different coverings and different numbers of legs or pictures of animals cut from magazines

2 What to Do

Engage Display Flip Chart page 20. Read the title aloud as you track the text. Help children identify the pictured materials. (Animal picture cards) Then display one of the animal pictures and help children identify the animal. Ask: **What can you tell me about how this animal looks?**

Explore Divide children into small groups and provide each group with an assortment of animal picture cards. Have children take turns naming the pictured animals. Then have each child select one of the animal cards. Say: **Now look carefully at your animal. Tell what kind of covering your animal has.** Guide children to use words such as fur, hair, scales, feathers, and skin when describing their animals. Then say: **Now we will work together as a group to sort the animal cards. Look for skin coverings that are alike in one important way. Put animals that have the same skin coverings into the same group.**

Explain Guide children in describing the results. **How are the animals in one of your groups alike? How are the animals in your other group alike?** (Possible answer: All the animals in one group are covered with hair or fur. All the animals in the other group have smooth skin.)

Evaluate After children have finished sorting the animals by their coverings, hold up another picture card and say: **In which group does this animal belong? Why?** (Children's answers should reflect the covering of the animal shown in the picture.) Repeat children's answers using complete sentences. Then have children repeat the sentences after you.

Extend Repeat the investigation by having children sort the pictures in a different way. You may wish to suggest that they look at whether the animals have legs when sorting them. Alternatively, they can classify animals by their size or their color. Once children have finished sorting, have them suggest labels for each group for you to write on index cards.

3 Discuss the Results

1. **Observe** What can you learn about animals by looking at pictures of them? (Possible answer: You can learn about different animal body coverings and body parts.)

2. **Classify** What do you look for when sorting animals into groups? (You look for ways in which animals are alike and put those animals into the same group.)

Go Further Tell children you have a friend who has a cat, a dog, a goldfish, and a hamster. **How would you put these pets into groups by their body coverings?** (The dog, cat, and hamster are all covered with fur. The goldfish is covered with scales.) **How would you put these pets into groups by their legs?** (The cat, dog, and hamster have legs. The fish does not have legs.) **What information would you need to know if you wanted to sort these animals by color?** (You would have to know the color of the animals' fur and scales.) Repeat children's responses using complete sentences and have them repeat the sentences.

Process Skills

Tell children that they are **communicating** when they tell what animals look like. Explain that when they put animals together based on how their bodies look, they are **classifying** the animals into groups.

Listening and Speaking Tip

• Remind children that it is important to listen politely when others speak. Tell them to look directly at the speaker and to try to keep their bodies still as they listen. Remind them that they need to raise their hands and wait to be called on before they begin to speak.

Lesson 9

What can you tell about animals?

Objectives

Children will:
- Identify characteristics of insects, birds, fish, and reptiles.

You need: Flip Chart pages 19, 21

Build Background

Remind children that in the previous lessons they learned about different places that plants grow. Help them recall these places as a desert, a forest, a farm, and a garden. Explain that animals also live in these and other places. Name each place and ask children what animals they might see living there.

Circle Time!

Sing "Look at the Horse and the Eagle"
- Bring children to the circle by singing "Look at the Horse and the Eagle" on Flip Chart page 19.

- As children come to the circle and sit, track the words on the chart with your finger and encourage children to sing along. Sing the song again once everyone is sitting.

Talk About It!

- Use Flip Chart page 21 to review vocabulary terms before you begin to teach Lesson 9.

- Guide **oral vocabulary** development by asking the following questions: **What kind of covering do birds have?** (Feathers) **What body part helps birds move?** (Wings) **Does an insect have a few or many legs? What else does this insect have that could help it get around?** (Wings) **Which animal lives in water?** (Fish) **What kind of body covering does a fish have?** (Scales) **What does a fish use to help it move through the water?** (Fins) **What kind of body covering does a lizard have?** (Scales) Remind children to answer using complete sentences.

Learn About It!

- Use **Teacher Instructions** at the bottom of Flip Chart page 21 to guide the science lesson. Children should understand that there are different types of animals each with its own characteristics.

Vocabulary

insect: a very small animal with six legs and three body parts

bird: an animal that has feathers, wings, two legs, and hatches from an egg

fish: animals that live in water and have gills

lizard: a reptile with four legs and skin covered with scales

wings: parts of a bird's body that it uses to fly

fins: parts of a fish's body that help it move through the water

52 *Unit A • Life Science*

Science Background
Fins and Legs

Children may mistakenly think that all animals that live in water have fins. Explain that most turtles, for example, live in the water part of the time and they do not have fins. Turtles have legs that they use to swim in water and walk on land.

- Have children use the picture clues and answer the questions. Expand on children's responses by using them in complete sentences. Prompt children to repeat the sentences.

- Call on volunteers to circle and put an X on the appropriate pictures.

- Continue questioning by asking the following: **If you saw an animal with six legs crawling in your garden, what could you tell about it? Why?** (Possible answer: It is an insect because all insects have six legs.) **What is one thing that birds and most insects have?** (They have wings.)

- Have children explain their answer for the **Compare/Contrast** question. (They have scales)

Differentiate Instruction

Full Day or Extended Instruction

- Provide children with small paper bags, construction paper, feathers, pipe cleaners, crayons, scissors, and paste. Tell them that they will each choose one animal and use the materials to make a hand puppet. You may wish to model how to make a simple bird or fish puppet.

- As children work remind them to include the appropriate body covering for their animal puppet and body parts.

Reteaching and English Language Learner Support

- Reinforce the words *insect, bird, fish, lizard, wings,* and *fins* by displaying a picture of each animal or animal body part. Help children identify each picture.

- Display a picture of an unfamiliar animal that is a bird, a fish, or an insect. Have children use what they know about animals to tell what type of animal they think it is.

Science Centers

Monitor Progress

- Use "Talk About It," "Learn About It," and Centers activities to check children's progress through the week.

- Refer to "Differentiate Instruction" for reteaching tips.

- Use Assessment Sheet on Teacher's Edition page 145 to record each child's understanding of concepts covered in this lesson.

Center 1: Science Song "Look at the Horse and the Eagle"
Play "Look at the Horse and the Eagle" for the children in the listening center. Encourage children to sing along. Provide each child with a copy of the song to track words, illustrate, and take home to share, as appropriate.

Center 2: Cross-Curricular Link
Art Provide children with paper and tempera paints and brushes or finger paints. Have children paint large fish. Encourage them to remember to include the fish's tail and its fins. Then encourage children to decorate their fish with different colored patterns of dots or stripes. Have children take turns displaying their fish and talking about the patterns.

Center 3: Science Journal

Ask children to draw a picture of an animal that they would like to learn more about. Have each child dictate a label.

How do animals move?

Objectives

Children will:
· Identify different ways that animals move.

You need: Flip Chart pages 19, 22

Build Background

Ask children if they have ever seen a frog. Invite a volunteer to show how a frog moves. Then repeat by having children tell and show how a dog moves. Explain that in this lesson, they will explore ways that other animals move.

Circle Time!

Sing "Look at the Horse and the Eagle"

· Bring children to the circle by singing "Look at the Horse and the Eagle" on Flip Chart page 19.

· As children come to the circle and sit, track the words on the chart with your finger and encourage children to sing along. Sing the song again once everyone is sitting.

Vocabulary

hop: to jump, or move by jumping

fly: to move through the air with wings

run: to move legs very fast

swim: to move along on or in the water

Talk About It!

· Use Flip Chart page 22 to review vocabulary terms before you begin to teach Lesson 10.

· Guide **oral vocabulary** development by asking these questions: **Which picture shows an animal swimming?** (Fish) **How does the horse move?** (Runs, trots) **What body part helps a bird to fly?** (Wings) **How is the kangaroo moving?** (Hopping) Remind children to answer using complete sentences.

Learn About It!

· Use **Teacher Instructions** at the bottom of Flip Chart page 22 to guide the science lesson. Identify the animals as kangaroos, horses, an eagle, and fish. Children should understand that animals use their body parts to move in different ways.

· Have children use the picture clues and answer the questions. Expand on children's responses by using them in complete sentences. Prompt children to repeat the sentences.

· Call on volunteers to circle and put an X on the appropriate pictures.

· Continue questioning by asking the following: **What can both the bird and** the fish do? (Possible answer: They can both use their bodies to move.) **What is one thing that birds can do that fish cannot do?** (Birds can fly and fish cannot.)

- Have children explain their answer for the **Infer** question. (Run, walk)

Differentiate Instruction

Full Day or Extended Instruction

- Provide children with picture cards of animals that move in different ways. Have children display their animals and name them. Then have children sort their cards by how animals move: fly, run swim, hop.

- Gather children in a circle and have them take turns showing their animal card, telling how the animal moves, and then placing the card in the correct "pile."

Reteaching and English Language Learner Support

- Reinforce the words *hop, fly, run, swim,* by saying each word and having children act it out.

- Point to each picture on Flip Chart page 22. Help children summarize the different ways that animals can move by having them complete this sentence frame to describe each animal's movements: "A _____ uses its _____ to _____."

Science Centers

Center 1: Science Song "Look at the Horse and the Eagle"
Play "Look at the Horse and the Eagle" for the children in the listening center. Encourage children to sing along. Provide each child with a copy of the song to track words, illustrate, and take home to share, as appropriate.

Center 2: Cross-Curricular Link
Math Provide an assortment of animal picture cards that show animals with no feet (Snakes, worms), one foot (Snails), two feet (Birds), four feet (Most mammals and many reptiles and amphibians) and six feet (Insects). Depending on children's counting skills, you can ask them to sort the animals into two groups—those with few feet and those with many feet—or you can challenge them to sort the animals into different groups by their number of feet.

Center 3: Science Journal
Ask children to think about their favorite animal. **What animal would you like to be for a day?** Invite children to draw a picture showing that animal. Have each child explain their choices.

Monitor Progress

- Use "Talk About It," "Learn About It," and Centers activities to check children's progress through the week.

- Refer to "Differentiate Instruction" for reteaching tips.

- Use Assessment Sheet on Teacher's Edition page 145 to record each child's understanding of concepts covered in this lesson.

How are animals alike and different?

Objectives

Children will:
- Identify how baby animals and adult animals are alike and different.
- Know names for young animals.

You need: Flip Chart pages 19, 23

Build Background

Display a picture of a mother cat and her kitten. Point to each and have children name it. Then ask: **How does a kitten look different from a grown-up cat?** (The kitten is much smaller.) Explain that in this lesson, they will explore ways that adult animals and their babies are the same and different.

Circle Time!

Sing "Look at the Horse and the Eagle"

- Bring children to the circle by singing "Look at the Horse and the Eagle" on Flip Chart page 19.

- As children come to the circle and sit, track the words on the chart with your finger and encourage children to sing along. Sing the song again once everyone is sitting.

> **Vocabulary**
> **alike:** being the same
> **different:** not being the same

Talk About It!

- Use Flip Chart page 23 to review vocabulary terms before you begin to teach Lesson 11.

- Guide vocabulary development by asking these questions: Point to the picture of the adult penguin. **Which picture shows another animal that looks the same? How do these two animals look alike?** Then point to the adult bear and the cubs. **What ways are these animals different?** (The cubs are smaller than the adult bear.) Repeat with the other animals. Remind children to answer using complete sentences.

Learn About It!

- Use **Teacher Instructions** at the bottom of Flip Chart page 23 to guide the science lesson.

- Guide children to identify the adult animals as a bear, a penguin, and a dog and the baby animals as a cub, a chick, and a puppy. Then have children match each adult animal with its baby. Children should understand that while young animals often look like their parents, they are smaller.

- Have children use the picture clues and answer the questions. Repeat the questions about each pair of adult and baby animals. Expand on children's responses by using them in complete sentences. Prompt children to repeat the sentences.

- Continue questioning by asking the following: **Think about how animals move. What other ways do you think these baby animals are different from their parents.** (Possible answer: They cannot move as quickly as their parents.)

- Have children explain their answer for the **Infer** question. (Possible answer: A fox because it has four legs, fur and lives in the forest)

Differentiate Instruction

Full Day or Extended Instruction

- Assemble pictures of grown-up and baby animals. Display each picture and help children identify each animal.

- Prepare a two-column chart. Label one side: **Adult Animals** and the other side **Baby Animals.** Have children paste their animal pictures in the appropriate columns. Then give each child a length of yarn. Have each child use the yarn to connect a grown-up and baby animal that go together. Help the child tape the two ends of the yarn in place. Help the child name the baby and the adult animals.

Reteaching and English Language Learner Support

- Reinforce the words *alike* and *different* by displaying three animal cards. Two cards should show an adult and a baby animal. The other card should show a completely different animal. Have children point to the two animals that are alike. Name the animals for children and have them repeat the names. Continue with other sets. Then have them point to the animal that is different.

Science Centers

Center 1: Science Song "Look at the Horse and the Eagle"
Play "Look at the Horse and the Eagle" for the children in the listening center. Encourage children to sing along. Provide each child with a copy of the song to track words, illustrate, and take home to share, as appropriate.

Center 2: Cross-Curricular Link
Physical Education Play a version of "Duck, Duck, Goose." Have children sit in a circle. Explain the rules. Begin the game by walking around the circle, lightly tapping each child's head and saying "Bear." When you say "Cub," that child has to get up and run around the circle back to his or her space. Then that child walks around until he or she finds a new "Cub."

Center 3: Science Journal
Invite children to draw an adult and a baby animal they might see on a farm.

Monitor Progress
- Use "Talk About It," "Learn About It," and Centers activities to check children's progress through the week.
- Refer to "Differentiate Instruction" for reteaching tips.
- Use Assessment Sheet on Teacher's Edition page 146 to record each child's understanding of concepts covered in this lesson.

Where do animals live?

Objectives

Children will:
- Identify animal habitats.
- Understand that animals have different characteristics that enable them to live in different habitats.

You need: Flip Chart pages 19, 24

Build Background

Remind children that when they learned about plants, they learned that plants lived in places like deserts, forests, farms, and gardens. Explain that animals can live in different places, too. Ask: **What kind of animals do you think you might see if you went for a walk in a park in your neighborhood?** (Possibilities include squirrels, chipmunks, dogs, birds.) **Where else might you go to see animals?** (Possible responses: You could see animals in a zoo, at the beach, in the forest, on a farm.)

Circle Time!

Sing "Look at the Horse and the Eagle"
- Bring children to the circle by singing "Look at the Horse and the Eagle" on Flip Chart page 19.

- As children come to the circle and sit, track the words on the chart with your finger and encourage children to sing along. Sing the song again once everyone is sitting.

Vocabulary

ocean: largest body of water with salt water

land: the part of the Earth's surface that is not covered by water

cold: having a low temperature

Talk About It!

- Use Flip Chart page 24 to review vocabulary terms before you begin to teach Lesson 12.

- Guide **oral vocabulary** development by asking these questions: Point to the picture of the ocean. **What animals live in this place?** (Fish) **What other animals do you know that live in the ocean?** (Dolphins, whales) **Which place do you think is very cold? Why?** (Place with ice) **Where does the coyote live, on land or in the ocean?** (Land) Remind children to answer using complete sentences.

Learn About It!

- Use **Teacher Instructions** at the bottom of Flip Chart page 23 to guide the science lesson. Guide children to describe each environment. Point out that ocean water is salty, and so different animals live in oceans than

Science Background

Environments and Habitats

An ecosystem is made up of the community of plants and animals and the environment in which they live. The place or environment in which a plant or an animal usually lives is termed its habitat. A habitat satisfies all the basic needs of a living thing. Environments have different landforms, climates, and plant and animal life. Environments also have both living and nonliving parts.

in fresh water found in lakes, ponds, rivers, and streams. Point out special adaptations that animals have to help them live in different places: (The polar bear has huge feet shaped like snowshoes to help it walk over the snow. It has a heavy coat and a thick layer of fat to keep it warm.)

- Have children use the picture clues and answer the questions. Expand on children's responses by using them in complete sentences. Prompt children to repeat the sentences.

- Call on volunteers to circle and put an X on the appropriate pictures.

- Continue questioning by asking the following: **What might happen to the coyote if you took it to a very cold place to live like the polar bear's home?** (Possible answer: It might get too cold because it does not have very thick fur as does the polar bear.)

- Have children explain their answer for the **Compare** question.

Differentiate Instruction

Full Day or Extended Instruction

- Provide children with old magazines and scissors. Help them find and cut out pictures of animals that live on land, in the ocean, and in cold places.

- Prepare a three-column chart. Title the chart **"Where Animals Live."** Label the columns with these headers: **Land, Ocean,** and **Cold Place**. Call on children, one at a time, to paste their animal picture in the correct column.

Reteaching and English Language Learner Support

- Reinforce the words *ocean, land,* and *cold* by displaying pictures that show these places. Say each word and have children point to the picture that is named by the word.

- Display a globe. Help children point to areas that are land. Then have them point to areas that are ocean. Point out that the coldest areas of Earth are called the North Pole and the South Pole.

Science Centers

Monitor Progress

- Use "Talk About It," "Learn About It," and Centers activities to check children's progress through the week.
- Refer to "Differentiate Instruction" for reteaching tips.
- Use Assessment Sheet on Teacher's Edition page 146 to record each child's understanding of concepts covered in this lesson.

Center 1: Science Song "Look at the Horse and the Eagle"

Play "Look at the Horse and the Eagle" for the children in the listening center. Encourage children to sing along. Provide each child with a copy of the song to track words, illustrate, and take home to share, as appropriate.

Center 2: Cross-Curricular Link

Drama Have children choose an animal. Then call on a volunteer to give clues about his or her animal's identify by pantomiming how the animal moves and describing where the animal lives, what it eats, and its covering. The child who correctly guesses can be the next one to present a mystery animal.

Center 3: Science Journal

Invite children to draw another animal that lives in the ocean, on the land, or in a cold place. Have children dictate a sentence that includes the name of their animal and where it lives.

How can you show different animal homes?

Objective

Children will:
- Explain that animals meet their need for shelter in different ways.
- Identify specific shelters used by different animals.
- Children will identify the homes of different animals.

1 Build Background

This activity helps children think about what kinds of homes different animals build or find.

Managing Time and Materials

Time: 15 minutes
Grouping: individuals or partners

Materials: Flip Chart page 25 old magazines, crayons, scissors, construction paper, tape

2 What to Do

Engage Display Flip Chart Page 25. Read the title aloud as you track the text. Help children identify the pictured materials. (Magazines, crayons, scissors, construction paper, tape) Then focus attention on the whale swimming in the ocean. Ask: **What can you tell me about where this animal makes its home?** (A fish makes its home in the ocean.) Repeat this procedure with the bird. (Most birds make their homes in a tree.)

Explore Distribute materials and have children look for pictures showing animals in their homes. When they find a picture say: **Now cut out your picture. Then <u>tape</u> it to a piece of construction paper.** Then say: **Now look carefully at your animal. <u>Tell</u> what kind of home your animal has.** Guide children to use words such as *tree, nest, hive, hole, burrow, cave, pond, lake, ocean,* or *river* when identifying animal homes.

Explain Guide children in describing the results. Invite each child to display his or her picture, identify the animal, and tell where it lives. Encourage them to describe which animals made their homes and which animals found their homes in nature. Ask: **How does each animal's home help to keep it safe?** (Possible answer: It helps it hide from enemies. It protects it from the weather.)

Evaluate Display all the children's pictures in the chalkboard tray. **How are all the animals alike?** (Possible answer: All the animals have a home.) **How are all the animals different?** (They each live in a different kind of home.) Repeat children's answers using complete sentences. Then have children repeat the sentences after you.

Extend Have children use their pictures to create a mural. To do this divide a long sheet of mural paper into four sections. Use markers to sketch out and designate one section as the ocean, one section as a tree, one section as a hole or burrow, and one section as a pond. Help children place their pictures where they belong on the mural.

3 Discuss the Results

1. **Observe** What can you learn about animals by looking at pictures that show them in their homes? (Possible answer: You can learn what their homes look like. You can learn what their homes are made of.)

2. **Infer** Why do you think some animals live high up in a tree? (Living up high in a tree would keep the animal safe from animals on the ground.) **How do you think these animals reach their homes high in the treetops?** (They have to fly or be able to climb up the tree.)

Go Further Invite children to choose one of the animals whose homes they modeled. Have them act out how the animal builds or finds its home. Guide children's dramatizations by saying things such as: **Show how parent birds find twigs and straw to build a nest. Now show how the mother bird sits on the eggs in her nest. Now show how the baby birds learn to fly once they are ready to leave the nest.**

Process Skills

Tell children that they are **communicating** when they tell about where an animal makes its home. Explain that they are **making a model** when they draw or cut out pictures showing an animal in its home.

Listening and Speaking Tip

- Remind children that when they speak in front of the class, it is important to look at their listeners and keep their hands away from their mouths as they talk. Remind them to speak slowly and clearly as they tell about animals and their homes.

Notes

Unit B Earth Science

Introduce the Unit

- Introduce the unit of Earth Science by showing children Flip Chart page 26. Discuss with children what they see in the photograph by asking:

- **Where are the rocks?** Have volunteers circle the rocks.

- **Where are the mountains?** Have volunteers put an X on the mountains.

- **What else do you see in the photograph?** Encourage children to share what they know about hills, rocks, and plants.

- Explain to children that in this unit, they will learn about different places on Earth.

Introduce the Floor Puzzle

- Tell children that they will put together a puzzle that looks just like the photograph on Flip Chart page 26.

- Place the puzzle pieces on the floor and invite children to work as a group to put the puzzle together. Tell them that they can use the photograph on the flip chart to help them. Provide assistance as needed.

- As children are working on the puzzle, ask the following questions:
  Where are the mountains?
  Where is the water?
  What color is the sky?

- Explain to children that the puzzle will be in the Science Center. They will have other opportunities to put the puzzle together again and discuss the picture on the puzzle as they learn more about **Earth Science.**

Unit B: Earth Science

Materials List for Unit B

Activities	Kit materials	School-supplied materials
What is the weather like? pp. 72–73	thermometer, Demonstration type, for Extend activity	drawing paper markers
What is in soil and sand? pp. 82–83	paper plates hand lens plastic spoon loam soil sand	
How can water move? pp. 92–93	plastic dropper plastic tray plastic cup waxed paper (9 x 12 in.)	water paper towel tape (teacher use)
How can you reuse something? pp. 100–101		shapes precut from construction paper glue other decorations empty water bottles

Unit B Bibliography

Teachers may want to share the following books with children to expand their comprehension of science concepts taught in Unit B.

You may wish to place some or all of these books in the Science Center after reading them aloud to children.

An Ocean World
by Peter Sis
[Greenwillow Books, ISBN 0-688-09068-0,1992]
This nearly wordless book provides a snapshot of one whale's life in the ocean.

Galoshes
by Kit Allen
[Houghton Mifflin, ISBN 0-618-22997-3,2003]
An easy-to –read story about what to wear on a rainy, spring day and what to do during the day.

Here Comes Spring
by Mark Murphy
[Dorling Kindersley Publishing, Inc.
ISBN 0-7894-3484-9, 1999]
This children's book follows two dogs through the four seasons.

Let's Go Rock Collecting
by Roma Gans
[HarperCollins, ISBN 0-06-027283-X, 1997]
This book teaches children about rocks all over the world.

Longjohns
by Kit Allen
[Houghton Mifflin, ISBN 0-618-22996-5,2003]
This easy-to-read book explains to children the different layers of clothing needed on a winter day

Rocks, Rocks Big & Small
by Joanne Barkan
[Silver Press, ISBN 0-671-68660-7, 1990]
This book investigates where rocks come from. **Challenge**

Shapes in Nature
by Judy Feldman
[Children's Press, ISBN 0-516-05102-4, 1991]
This wordless picture book correlates common shapes to plants, animals, and other objects in nature.

Shooting Stars
by Franklyn M. Branley
[HarperTrophy, ISBN 0-06-445103-8,1989]
This book tells children about the secrets of shooting stars that light up the sky. **Challenge**

Snow!
by Christine Ford
[Harper Festival, ISBN 0-694-0199-1,1999]
This rhyming storybook explores winter snow.

Sweater
by Kit Allen
[Houghton Mifflin, ISBN 0-618-267370-5, 2003]
This book shows children what they need to wear on a fall day and what fun there is to be had outside.

Swimsuit
by Kit Allen
[Houghton Mifflin, ISBN 0-618-26371-3, 2003]
This easy-to-read story shows children what they need to wear on a hot summer day.

Weather
by Seymour Simon
[HarperCollins, ISBN 0-6881-7521-X, 2000]
This book looks at different weather patterns and how these patterns can be predicted by noticing specific sounds and sights. **Challenge**

What Makes Day and Night
by Franklyn M. Branley and Arthur Dorros
[HarperCollins, ISBN 0-690-04523-9, 1986]
This book includes photographs and drawings to explain night and day.

What the Moon is Like
by Franklyn M. Branley
[HarperCollins, ISBN 0—027993-1, 2000]
This book introduces children to the Moon.

Why Do Leaves Change Color?
by Betsy Maestro
[HarperCollins, ISBN 0-06-022874-4,1994]
An easy-to-read book explaining why leaves change color.

Unit B: Planning Guide

Lesson/Activity	Pacing	Science Objectives/Vocabulary
Activity What is the weather like? pp. 72–73	20 minutes	Children will discuss and compare the weather in different locations.
13 What are different kinds of weather? pp. 74–75	20 minutes	Children will identify different kinds of weather. sunny, rainy, windy, snowy, cloudy
14 What can you wear in different weather? pp. 76–77	20 minutes	Children will describe how changes in the weather affect their lives. clothes, outside, hot, warm
15 What are the seasons? pp. 78–79	20 minutes	Children will identify the four seasons. spring, summer, fall, winter
Activity What is in soil and sand? pp. 82–83	15 minutes	Children will identify sand and soil samples.
16 What covers Earth? pp. 84–85	20 minutes	Children will understand that land and water cover Earth's surface. rocks, Earth, sand
17 What are different places on Earth? pp. 86–87	20 minutes	Children will identify landforms. mountain, valley, plain, canyon
18 What is in the sky? pp. 88–89	20 minutes	Children will describe the night sky and the day sky. Moon, stars, Sun, day, night, sky

Lesson/Activity	Pacing	Science Objectives/Vocabulary
Activity How can water move? pp. 92–93	15 minutes	Children will demonstrate that water flows down a slope.
19 Where is water on Earth? pp. 94–95	20 minutes	Children will identify bodies of water. ice, sea, lake, river
20 How do people use land? pp. 96–97	20 minutes	Children will describe how people use land to meet their needs. build, wood
21 How can we help care for Earth? pp. 98–99	20 minutes	Children will understand the terms *reuse*, *recycle*, and *reduce*. reuse, recycle, reduce, protect
Activity How can you reuse something? pp. 100–101	20 minutes	Children will demonstrate that some things can be reused.
ASSESSMENT pp. 147–148		

Science Songs and Poems

Objective

Children will:
• Sing a song to develop oral language.
• Identify the four seasons.
• Recognize that different kinds of clothing are worn during each season.

You need: Flip Chart page 27, dinosaur puppet

1 Build Background

Begin a discussion about the kinds of clothing that children wear in different kinds of weather. Help children identify the four seasons: fall, winter, spring and summer. Invite children to tell about their favorite season and what they like to wear during that time of year.

2 What to Do

• Tell children that they will learn a song today. Have children listen as you hum the tune of "Jack and Jill." Hum a few times and then invite children to hum along with you.

• When children are ready, sing "Clothes by the Season" to the tune of "Jack and Jill." Sing the verse several times, inviting children to sing with you.

• Direct children's attention to Flip Chart page 27 and have children discuss the picture. Prompt children as needed with questions.

• Then sing the song again using "Annie" the dinosaur puppet.

• Call on volunteers to tell why someone would wear a sweater in the fall, a heavy coat in the winter, boots in the rain, or sandals in the summer.

3 Talk About It

• Point to the words *sweater, coat, boots,* and *sandals* in the song. Say each word and have children repeat it after you. Tell children that these words tell about different kinds of clothing.

• Invite volunteers to use each word in their own sentences.

You may also wish to teach children the following poems and finger plays with these lessons.

(Lessons 13–14)

Pitter-patter raindrops,
Falling from the sky;
(Wiggle fingers to imitate falling rain.)
Here is my umbrella
To keep me safe and dry.
(Place hands over head.)

When the rain is over,
And the sun begins to glow,
(Make a large circle with hands.)
Little flowers start to bud,
(Cup hands together.)
And grow and grow and grow!
(Slowly spread hands apart.)

(Lesson 15)

Seasons

In the spring leaves are growing,
Green, green leaves are growing.
In the spring leaves are growing,
Growing on the trees.

In the summer leaves are rustling,
Green, green leaves are rustling.
In the summer leaves are rustling,
Rustling in the trees.

In the fall leaves are dropping,
Brown, brown leaves are dropping.
In the fall leaves are dropping,
Dropping from the trees.

In the winter leaves are missing,
Brown, brown leaves are missing.
In the winter leaves are missing,
Missing from the trees.

Activity

What is the weather like?

Objective

Children will:
• Discuss and compare the weather in different locations.

1 Build Background

This activity helps children understand that weather can change depending on locations.

Managing Time and Materials

Time: 20 minutes
Grouping: whole class

Materials: Flip Chart page, 28 paper, markers, large thermometer

2 What to Do

Engage Display Flip Chart page 28 and read the title aloud. Help children identify the objects pictured. Ask questions under **Build Background** at the bottom of Flip Chart page 28. Then say: **Today we will talk about the weather.** Then ask a volunteer to circle the picture on the flip chart that shows it is cold outside. Distribute materials to each child and say: **We will draw a picture to show what the weather is like today.**

Explore If possible, take children outdoors and have them decide what the weather is like. Prompt them with questions: **Is it hot today? Is it windy? How does the air feel?** Have children first stand in a shady spot and in a sunny spot. Discuss the differences in air temperature. Back in the classroom, have children draw a picture to show today's weather.

Weather

• Weather occurs in the air that surrounds Earth. Conditions in the air determine whether the weather is cloudy or clear, windy or calm.

• The Sun's energy warms the air and causes the air temperature to rise and to fall.

Listening and Speaking Tip

• Remind children to raise their hands when they want to ask or answer a question. They should not call out questions and answers before being called upon.

• Invite a volunteer to model this behavior and then call on him or her for a comment.

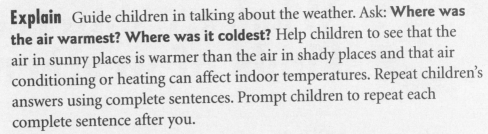

Explain Guide children in talking about the weather. Ask: **Where was the air warmest? Where was it coldest?** Help children to see that the air in sunny places is warmer than the air in shady places and that air conditioning or heating can affect indoor temperatures. Repeat children's answers using complete sentences. Prompt children to repeat each complete sentence after you.

Evaluate Have children predict what the weather will be like tomorrow. Discuss with children that the weather changes from day to day and knowing what the weather is like today can often help people make a good guess about what it will be the following day.

Extend Display the large thermometer and have children say the word after you. Explain that a thermometer is often used to measure how hot or cold the air temperature is. Point out the red ribbon and explain that this stands for the red liquid inside a real thermometer. Tell children that the liquid goes up in the tube when the air is hot. Then demonstrate by pretending to measure the temperature.

3 Discuss the Results

1. **Measure** Why do we need to know the temperature? (It can help you decide what kind of clothing to wear.)

2. **Predict** What information can help you predict what tomorrow's weather will be like? (Today's weather can often help you figure out what tomorrow's weather will be.)

Go Further Help children record outdoor weather observations for a week or a month on a calendar.

Process Skills

Tell children that they can make **observations** about the weather by looking outdoors. Explain that when they talk about their weather observations, they are **communicating** their findings to others.

What are different kinds of weather?

Objectives

Children will:
- Identify different kinds of weather.
- Understand the characteristics of each kind of weather.

You need: Flip Chart pages 27, 29

Build Background

Have children describe what they like to do when the day is sunny; rainy; windy; or snowy. If children are unfamiliar with snow, explain that snow and ice are different forms of water.

Circle Time!

Sing "Clothes by the Season"

- Bring children to the circle by singing the song on Flip Chart page 27.
- As children come to the circle and sit, track the words on the chart with your finger and encourage children to sing along. Sing the song again once everyone is sitting.

Vocabulary

sunny: to have bright sunshine

rainy: to have a lot of rain

windy: to have a lot of wind

snowy: to have a lot of snow

cloudy: to have a lot of clouds

Talk About It!

- Use Flip Chart page 29 to review vocabulary terms before you begin to teach Lesson 13.
- Guide **oral vocabulary** development by asking the following questions: **What do you see in the sky when it is sunny?** (Sun) **What falls from the sky when it is rainy?** (Rain) **How can you tell when it is windy?** (The leaves blow) **What do you see on the ground when it is snowy?** (Snow) Remind children to answer using complete sentences.

Learn About It!

- Use Teacher Instructions at the bottom of Flip Chart page 29. Children should understand that there are many kinds of weather that can be described by words such as *sunny, rainy, windy,* and *snowy*. The weather is constantly changing.
- Have children use the picture clues and answer the questions. Expand on children's responses by using complete sentences. Prompt children to repeat your sentences.

- Call on volunteers to circle and put an X on the appropriate pictures.
- Continue questioning by asking: **How would you describe the weather if there were lots of clouds?** (You could say it was cloudy weather.)
- Have children share their answer to the **Sequence** question. (The sun)

Differentiate Instruction

Full Day or Extended Instruction

- Distribute old magazines and scissors to children. Help each child cut out a picture that shows what the weather can be like.
- Tape up a large piece of butcher paper divided into four columns. Title the columns **Sunny, Rainy, Windy,** and **Snowy**.
- Read aloud one of the headings and invite children whose picture shows that kind of weather to paste their pictures in the correct column. Ask them to identify what picture clues helped them to determine the weather.
- Then challenge the group to point to the column that best shows today's weather.

Reteaching and English Language Learner Support

- Display pictures of different kinds of weather. Give simple directions such as: **Point to the picture that shows a sunny day.**
- Then ask children yes/no questions about the weather shown in the picture. For example: **Does this picture show a windy day?**

Science Centers

Center 1: Science Song "Clothes by the Season"
Play the song for the children. Encourage children to sing along. Provide each child with a copy of the song to track words, illustrate, and take home to share, as appropriate.

Center 2: Cross-Curricular Link
Art Before the activity, place some cotton balls in a large paper bag and shake with black tempera paint powder to make gray clouds. Then distribute gray and white cotton balls and gray and blue construction paper, white glue, and crayons. Have children use the cotton balls to create cloud pictures that show a rainy day and a sunny day. Encourage them to talk about their pictures by saying: "The weather in this picture is _____."

Center 3: Science Journal
Ask children to draw pictures of their favorite kind of weather in their **Discovery Journal.** Have children dictate a word or a sentence about their picture.

Monitor Progress

• Use "Talk About It," "Learn About It," and Centers activities to check children's progress through the week.

• Refer to "Differentiate Instruction" for reteaching tips.

• Use Assessment Sheet on Teacher's Edition page 147 to record each child's understanding of concepts covered in this lesson.

What can you wear in different kinds of weather?

Objectives

Children will:
- Describe how changes in the weather affect their lives.
- Choose clothing that is appropriate for the weather.

You need: Flip Chart pages 27, 30

Build Background

Have children recall words that tell about the weather. Then invite them to tell what the weather was like when they came to school. Invite volunteers to go to their cubbies to show what they wore. Then ask if the weather is nice enough for them to go outside during recess or whether they will have to play indoors. Encourage them to explain why they think as they do.

Circle Time!

Sing "Clothes by the Season"

- Bring children to the circle by singing the song on Flip Chart page 27.
- As children come to the circle and sit, track the words on the chart with your finger and encourage children to sing along. Sing the song again once everyone is sitting.

Talk About It!

- Use Flip Chart page 30 to review vocabulary terms before you begin to teach Lesson 14.

- Guide **oral vocabulary** development by asking the following questions. **What do we call things we wear?** (Clothes) **Are the clothes on the Flip Chart things that we wear outside or inside?** (Outside) **Why do people wear rubber boots when it rains?** (To make sure their feet stay dry) Remind children to answer using complete sentences.

Learn About It!

- Use Teacher Instructions at the bottom of Flip Chart page 30. Children should understand that changes in the weather may determine their activities and what they wear to stay warm in snowy or cold weather, cool in warm and hot weather, and dry in rainy weather.

Vocabulary

clothes: things that are worn on the body

outside: outdoors

hot: having a high temperature

warm: more hot than cold

- Have children use the picture clues and answer the questions. Expand on children's responses by using complete sentences. Prompt children to repeat your sentences.
- Call on volunteers to circle and put an X on the appropriate pictures.
- Continue questioning by asking: **Why do we wear heavy clothes outdoors on a cold day?** (Possible answer: Heavy clothes keep us warm when it is cold outside.) **Why do we wear raincoats, boots, and rain hats on rainy days?** (Possible answer: These clothes keep us dry when it rains.)
- Have children explain their answer to the **Draw Conclusion** question. (Possible answer: I would wear boots to keep my feet dry and warm.)

Differentiate Instruction

Full Day or Extended Instruction
- Distribute old catalogs to groups of children. Have children look for pictures of clothing that they would wear in hot weather, warm weather and cold weather.

Reteaching and English Language Learner Support
- Have children look at Flip Chart page 30 again. Play a game of "I Spy" using weather clues to help them identify clothing; for example: "I spy something to wear on my feet on a rainy day." Once the mystery item is identified, have children share something they could do on a rainy day.

Science Centers

Center 1: Science Song "Clothes by the Season"
Play the song for the children. Encourage children to sing along. Provide each child with a copy of the song to track words, illustrate, and take home to share, as appropriate.

Center 2: Cross-Curricular Link
Language Arts Teach children this rhyme and have them chant it. Call on volunteers to chime in on the third line telling what kind of clothing they would wear. Conclude by having them describe what activities they would do given the weather:

Come outside and play with me!
The weather is (Name weather) as you can see!
I'll wear a (Name garment) and a (Name garment), too.
We'll have fun; just we two!

Center 3: Science Journal
Ask children to draw pictures of themselves playing outside in their favorite kind of weather. Before they draw, remind them to think about the clothing they would wear.

Monitor Progress
- Use "Talk About It," "Learn About It," and Centers activities to check children's progress through the week.
- Refer to "Differentiate Instruction" for reteaching tips.
- Use Assessment Sheet on Teacher's Edition page 147 to record each child's understanding of concepts covered in this lesson.

What are the seasons?

Objectives

Children will:
- Identify the four seasons.
- Describe the weather and other characteristics of the seasons.

You need: Flip Chart pages 27, 31, dinosaur puppet

Build Background

Have children tell their favorite time of year and describe what the weather is like during that time of year. Explain that the year is divided into four parts called seasons: spring, summer, fall, and winter. Each season has special things about it that help us know what time of year it is.

Circle Time!

Sing "Clothes for the Season"
- Bring children to the circle by singing the song on Flip Chart page 27.
- As children come to the circle and sit, track the words on the chart with your finger and encourage children to sing along. Sing the song again once everyone is sitting using the dinosaur puppet.

Vocabulary

spring: season after winter when plants begin to grow

summer: season after spring when weather is the warmest

fall: season between summer and winter when many leaves turn color

winter: season after fall when weather is the coldest

Talk About It!

- Use Flip Chart page 31 to review vocabulary terms before you begin to teach Lesson 15.
- Guide **oral vocabulary** development by asking the following questions as you point to the trees. **On which trees do the leaves look as if they are growing?** (Spring, summer) **On which tree do the leaves look as if they are getting ready to drop off?** (Fall) **On which tree have all the leaves disappeared?** (Winter) Remind children to answer using complete sentences.

Learn About It!

- Use Teacher Instructions at the bottom of Flip Chart page 31. Children should understand that the seasons come in the same order every year and this pattern is repeated year after year—spring follows winter, summer follows spring, fall follows summer, and winter follows fall.
- Have children use the picture clues and answer the questions. Expand on children's responses by using complete sentences. Prompt children to repeat your sentences.

- Call on volunteers to circle and put an X on the appropriate pictures. Encourage them to explain how the appearance of the tree helps them figure out the season. If you live in a place with few seasonal changes, discuss this with children.

- Continue questioning by asking: **Why do you think the tree leaves are so small in the spring?** (Possible answer: The tree has just started growing again after winter.) **What do you notice about color of the leaves in the fall?** (They have changed from green to red.) Point out that this change in color shows that the leaves are about to drop off the tree.

- Discuss the meaning of the words *before* and *after*. Then have children answer the **Sequence** question. (Spring)

Differentiate Instruction

Full Day or Extended Instruction

- Take children on a walk around the *school grounds* or the neighborhood to notice signs of the season.

- Back in the classroom, invite children to dictate their observations. Record their observations on chart paper and read their sentences aloud.

- Distribute drawing paper and crayons and have children create illustrations to go with the experience story. Post the illustrated story and occasionally reread it with children. Repeat the activity when the season changes.

Reteaching and English Language Learner Support

- Point to each tree on Flip Chart page 31 as you name the season. Have children repeat the season after you.

- Name a season. Invite children to name an activity they enjoy during each season.

Science Centers

Center 1: Science Song "Clothes for the Season"
Play the song for the children. Encourage children to sing along. Provide each child with a copy of the song to track words, illustrate, and take home to share, as appropriate.

Center 2: Cross-Curricular Link
Language Arts Provide four pictures that each represent a season. Have children put the pictures in seasonal order beginning with spring. Then have them use the words *before* and *after* to describe when each season falls in the year. To guide children, provide this sentence frame for them to complete orally as they point to each picture:

"_____ comes before _____ and after _____."

Center 3: Science Journal
Choose a tree or large plant that is visible from the classroom window. Ask children to draw a picture of the tree showing what it looks like during the spring, the summer, the fall, or the winter. Have children display their finished pictures and identify the season.

Monitor Progress

- Use "Talk About It," "Learn About It," and Centers activities to check children's progress through the week.
- Refer to "Differentiate Instruction" for reteaching tips.
- Use Assessment Sheet on Teacher's Edition page 147 to record each child's understanding of concepts covered in this lesson.

Science Songs and Poems

> ## Objective
> Children will:
> • Sing a song to develop oral language.
> • Recognize that there are different kinds of landforms.
>
> **You need:** Flip Chart page 32, dinosaur puppet

1 Build Background

Begin a discussion about the different kinds of landforms on Earth by telling children that land has many different kinds of shapes. Tell children that a mountain is a high place, a valley is a low place between mountains, and a plain is flat land.

2 What to Do

• Tell children that they will learn a song today. Have children listen as you hum the tune of "Home on the Range." Hum a few times and then invite children to hum along with you.

• When children are ready, sing "Looking Down from the Sky" to the tune of "Home on the Range." Sing the verse several times, inviting children to sing with you.

• Direct children's attention to Flip Chart page 32 and have children discuss the picture. Prompt children as needed with questions.

• Then sing the song again using "Annie" the dinosaur puppet.

• Discuss the song by asking children which place they would like to visit and have them explain why.

3 Talk About It

• Point to the phrase *look down* in the song. Call on volunteers, in turn, to stand on a chair and pretend to be in a plane looking down. (Provide assistance as needed.)

• Then say: **Look down. What do you see?** Have children respond using a complete sentence. (Accept any reasonable response.)

You may also wish to teach children the following poems and finger plays with these lessons.

(Lesson 16)

Little drops of water,
Little grains of sand
Make the mighty ocean,
And the pleasant land.

(Lesson 17)

Around and about,
Around and about,
Over and under
And in and out.
Run through the valley,
Swim in the sea,
Climb up a mountain,
Much taller than a tree.

(Lesson 18)

At night I see the twinkling stars
    (Move fingers.)

And a great big shining moon.
    (Circle arms overhead.)

Then the sun comes up,
    (Raise clasped arms slowly.)

And the stars disappear.
    (Move hands behind back.)

I wonder where they go.
    (Place finger on forehead.)

What is in soil and sand?

Objectives

Children will:
- Identify sand and soil samples.
- Tell what soil and sand are made of.
- Describe differences between soil and sand.
- Understand that Earth's surface is made up of different types of solid materials.

1 Build Background

This activity helps children identify characteristics of sand and soil that make up Earth's surface.

Managing Time and Materials

Time: 15 minutes
Grouping: small groups

Materials: Flip Chart page 33
paper plates, sand, soil, plastic spoons, hand lense

2 What to Do

Engage Display Flip Chart page 33. Read the title aloud. Help children identify the objects shown on the chart as paper plates, soil, sand, plastic spoon, and a hand lens. Ask questions under **Build Background** at the bottom of Flip Chart page 33. Place the soil and sand samples on paper plates. Then say: **Today we will look at sand and soil to find out how they are the same and different.** Explain that Earth's surface is covered with soil, rocks, and sand. Then distribute the materials to each group and say: **We will look at soil first**. Have a volunteer come up and circle the soil sample on the Flip Chart.

Soil

• Soil is made up of small pieces of rocks, sand, clay, and decayed parts of plants and animals. Soil differs in color and texture. Light colored soil is usually sandy. Other soil is dark and very dense.

• Sand is made up of tiny bits of broken rock, shells, and coral. Beaches may have different kinds of rock around them making the sand different colors.

Explore Have children take turns looking at, feeling, and smelling the soil sample. Say: *Soil is another word for dirt.* **What can you tell us about the soil?** Encourage children to describe the color, texture, and smell of the soil sample as they use spoons to examine it. Have them identify anything that they see in the soil. Then repeat this procedure with sand. As children examine the sand on their plates, guide them to see that sand is made up of tiny rocks of different colors. Repeat children's answers using complete sentences. Prompt children to repeat each complete sentence after you.

Explain Guide children in describing the samples of soil and sand. As they talk about the samples, ask them to explain their answers. Encourage them to comment on how the samples look and feel.

Evaluate Have children compare and contrast the sand and soil samples. Ask: **How are sand and soil alike? How are sand and soil different? Which do you think is better for growing plants?** As children contrast the samples, remind them to comment on differences in how the samples looked and felt. (Children should observe that sand is lighter in color than soil, contains tiny bits of rock, and may feel rougher than soil. They should note that soil comes in different colors and textures, and may contain bits of leaves and twigs.)

Extend Repeat the activity and have children use a hand lens to observe each sample. Ask children what more they learned about each sample by using a hand lens.

Listening and Speaking Tip

• Tell children that it is important for all children to share their ideas.

• Remind them not to talk when others are talking and to listen carefully as others speak.

• Suggest that they wait until the speaker is finished talking before they ask questions.

3 Discuss the Results

1. **Observe** What can you learn about sand and soil when you look at it and touch it? (Answers may include its color, its texture, and objects that are found in it.)

2. **Tell** Where do we find sand and soil? (On Earth's surface)

Go Further Provide pots and have children place the samples in the pots. Have them pour the same amount of water in the pots. **Would sand or soil be better for growing plants that need a lot of water? Why?** (Soil because it holds water better than sand) Repeat children's responses using complete sentences and have them repeat the sentences.

Process Skills

Tell children that they can make **observations** about sand and soil by looking carefully at the samples. Explain that when they use their senses to make observations, they are **collecting data** on the samples.

What covers Earth?

Objectives

Children will:
- Understand that land and water cover Earth's surface.
- Identify the components of land as rocks, sand, and soil.

You need: Flip Chart pages 32, 34

Build Background

Have children tell where they have seen soil and sand before in the classroom. Remind children that sand is formed from tiny pieces of rock. Then challenge children to tell where they might go to see soil, sand, and rocks outside. Tell children that we live on Earth. Explain that Earth is a place that has land and water.

Circle Time!

Sing "Looking Down from the Sky"
- Bring children to the circle by singing the song on Flip Chart page 32.
- As children come to the circle and sit, track the words on the chart with your finger and encourage children to sing along. Sing the song again once everyone is sitting.

Vocabulary

rocks: pieces of stone

Earth: planet on which we live

sand: tiny grains of broken rock

Talk About It!

- Use Flip Chart page 34 to review vocabulary terms before you begin to teach Lesson 16.
- Guide **oral vocabulary** development by asking the following questions as you point to the pictures. **What do you see on the beach?** (Sand) **What do you think is on the ground under the grass, trees, and other plants growing in this park?** (Soil) Remind children to answer using complete sentences.

Learn About It!

- Use Teacher Instructions at the bottom of Flip Chart page 34. Children should understand that Earth's surface is covered by water and land. Land is made up of rock, sand, and soil.
- Have children use the picture clues and answer the questions. Expand on children's responses by using complete sentences. Prompt children to repeat your sentences.
- Call on volunteers to circle the rocks and put an X on the sand.

- Continue questioning by asking: **Where could you go in a park to see a lot of soil?** (Flower gardens and lawns have soil.)
- Have children explain their answer for the **Predict** question. (It gets muddy.)

Differentiate Instruction

Full Day or Extended Instruction
- Have small groups work at the sand table. Provide samples of soil and sand, a strainer, and a watering can. Have children sift the soil and sand to see what they contain.
- Then have children mound up the soil and sand samples, pour water on them, and observe what happens. Discuss which sample gets wet and muddy. Have them compare texture of wet soil and sand and dry soil and sand.

Reteaching and English Language Learner Support
- Display a photo of Earth from space. Have children point to Earth. Then have them point to land and water on Earth's surface.
- Have children summarize what they know about Earth's surface by using complete sentences. Provide a framework by having children orally complete these sentence frames: "Earth is covered with _____ and _____." "Land is made up of ____, ____, and ____."

Monitor Progress
- Use "Talk About It," "Learn About It," and Centers activities to check children's progress through the week.
- Refer to "Differentiate Instruction" for reteaching tips.
- Use Assessment Sheet on Teacher's Edition page 148 to record each child's understanding of concepts covered in this lesson.

Science Centers

Center 1: Science Song "Looking Down from the Sky"
Play the song for the children. Encourage children to sing along. Provide each child with a copy of the song to track words, illustrate, and take home to share, as appropriate.

Center 2: Cross-Curricular Link
Math Provide children with balance scales, rocks, and sand. Have children place a rock in one balance pan. Then have them find how much sand it would take to equal the mass of the rock. Demonstrate how to bring the pans into balance. Have them repeat this investigation with other rocks.

Center 3: Science Journal
Have children draw a picture showing what covers Earth. Have children show and tell about their pictures.

Lesson 17

What are different places on Earth?

Objectives

Children will:
- Identify landforms.
- Describe characteristics of landforms.

You need: Flip Chart pages 32, 35

Build Background

Remind children that the Earth is covered with water and land. Point out that the land that covers Earth has different shapes. Explain that mountains are one kind of land. Invite children to tell if they have ever visited a mountain. Ask: **Is a mountain a high or low place? What do you think you would be able to see if you climbed to the top of a mountain?**

Circle Time!

Sing "Looking Down from the Sky"
- Bring children to the circle by singing the song on Flip Chart page 32.
- As children come to the circle and sit, track the words on the chart with your finger and encourage children to sing along. Sing the song again once everyone is sitting.

Vocabulary

mountain: land that is higher than a hill

valley: low land between mountains

plain: flat land that stretches out in all directions

canyon: deep valley in rock carved by wind or water

Talk About It!

- Use Flip Chart page 35 to review vocabulary terms before you begin to teach Lesson 17.
- Guide **oral vocabulary** development by using your hand to show the meaning of the words *high*, *low*, and *flat*. **Which pictures show high places?** (Mountains) **Which picture shows a flat place?** (Plain) Remind children to answer using complete sentences.

Learn About It!

- Use Teacher Instructions at the bottom of Flip Chart page 35. Children should understand that land has different shapes and forms. Some landforms, like mountains, are high. Others, like valleys and canyons, are low. Some, like plains, are flat and extend in all directions.
- Have children use the picture clues and answer the questions. Expand on children's responses by using complete sentences. Prompt children to repeat your sentences.

Science Misconception

Characteristics of Mountain Tops

Children may think that all mountains have jagged tops. Tell children that some mountains have these tops, but others have rounded tops. To illustrate this point, display photos of the Rocky Mountains and the Appalachians. Ask children to tell how these two mountain ranges are the same and different.

- Continue questioning by asking: **How would you describe the shape of the land where we live?** (Possible response: The land has many mountains and valleys.) **Suppose you were a farmer. Would it be easier to grow plants on a mountain or on the plains?** (On the plains)

- Have children explain their answer to the **Infer** question. (Possible answer: It can be a good hiding place.)

Differentiate Instruction

Full Day or Extended Instruction

- Create a circle on the floor with masking tape and have children stand inside it. Explain that they will pretend to be in an airplane looking down at the landforms that they have learned about.

- Have children describe what they see below. Encourage them to use complete sentences.**Look at these tall mountains. They have jagged tops covered with snow. The sides of the mountain are very steep. Lots of trees grow on these sides.**

- Repeat this procedure for each landform.

Reteaching and English Language Learner Support

- Display a picture of a mountain, a valley, a plain, and a canyon. Help children identify each landform. Discuss each picture.

- Then ask children yes/no questions about each landform. For example: **Is a valley high? Is a canyon low?**

- Encourage children to tell what they know about different landforms.

Science Centers

Center 1: Science Song "Looking Down from the Sky"
Play the song for the children. Encourage children to sing along. Provide each child with a copy of the song to track words, illustrate, and take home to share, as appropriate.

Center 2: Cross-Curricular Link
Art Have children use modeling clay to make a mountain, valley, plain, or canyon.

Center 3: Science Journal
Ask children to draw a picture of a landform that they learned about in their **Discovery Journal**. Have children dictate a word or a sentence about their picture.

Monitor Progress

- Use "Talk About It," "Learn About It," and Centers activities to check children's progress through the week.

- Refer to "Differentiate Instruction" for reteaching tips.

- Use Assessment Sheet on Teacher's Edition page 148 to record each child's understanding of concepts covered in this lesson.

Lesson 18

What is in the sky?

Objectives

Children will:
- Describe the night sky and the day sky.
- Identify objects in the night and day sky.

You need: Flip Chart pages 32, 36

Build Background

Invite children to recall a time when they got up very early and a time when they went to bed very late. Ask: **Did you see the Sun come up? What happened to the sky at sunrise?** (It got bright.) **What did the sky look like when you went to bed?** (It was dark.)

Circle Time!

Sing "Looking Down from the Sky"
- Bring children to the circle by singing the song on Flip Chart page 32.
- As children come to the circle and sit, track the words on the chart with your finger and encourage children to sing along. Sing the song again once everyone is sitting.

Talk About It!

- Use Flip Chart page 36 to review vocabulary terms before you begin to teach Lesson 18.
- Guide **oral vocabulary** development by asking the following questions: **What gives us light during the day?** (Sun) **What gives us light on many nights?** (Moon) **What does the sky look like during the day?** (It is blue.) **What does the sky look like when the Sun goes down at night?** (It looks dark; black) Remind children to answer using complete sentences.

Learn About It!

- Use Teacher Instructions at the bottom of Flip Chart page 36. Children should understand that the night sky and the day sky are different colors, and that different things can be seen in each sky.
- Have children use the picture clues and answer the questions. Expand on children's responses by using complete sentences. Prompt children to repeat your sentences.
- Call on volunteers to circle and put an X on the appropriate pictures.

Vocabulary

Moon: an object in the sky; it travels around Earth and reflects the Sun's light

stars: any object appearing as a bright point in the sky at night; a mass of very hot gas

Sun: a bright object in the sky; closest star to Earth

day: the time of light between sunrise and sunset

night: the time between sunset and sunrises

sky: the area where clouds form; the space overhead that seems to cover Earth

- Explain that the Moon and stars are always in the sky even during the day, but the Sun is so bright that we cannot see the Moon or stars. Explain that the Sun is really a star that is a ball of burning gases. **What do we get from the Sun?** (Heat and light) Heat comes from the light of the Sun.

- Have children share their answer to the **Infer** question. (It gives us heat and light.)

Differentiate Instruction

Full Day or Extended Instruction

- Distribute pieces of light blue and very dark blue or black construction paper, crayons, and a piece of chalk.

- Ask children to hold up the piece of paper that is closest to the color of the night sky. Discuss what they might see in the night sky. Then using chalk, have them draw pictures of the moon and stars in the night sky.

- Repeat by discussing what children might see in the day sky.

Reteaching and English Language Learner Support

- Display pictures of the sky at night and during the day. Give simple directions such as: **Point to the picture that shows the sky at night. Point to the Moon. Point to the Sun.**

- Encourage children to summarize what they know about things in the sky at night and during the day. Model how to express ideas in complete sentences if necessary.

Science Centers

Center 1: Science Song "Looking Down from the Sky"
Play the song for the children. Encourage children to sing along. Provide each child with a copy of the song to track words, illustrate, and take home to share, as appropriate.

Center 2: Cross-Curricular Link
Math Have children recall which season of the year is warmest. Explain that summer is also the season that has longer days and short nights. Then have children identify which season is coldest. Have children infer whether winter days or nights are longer. Then display a demonstration clock and set the hands for 6 o'clock. Explain that this time shows when many people eat dinner. Discuss what the sky looks like at 6 pm. Continue by setting the clock for different times such as 5 AM, 8 AM, 10 PM.

Center 3: Science Journal
Ask children to use their star stickers to "draw" a picture of a night sky in their **Discovery Journal.** Have children dictate a sentence about their picture.

Monitor Progress

- Use "Talk About It," "Learn About It," and Centers activities to check children's progress through the week.
- Refer to "Differentiate Instruction" for reteaching tips.
- Use Assessment Sheet on Teacher's Edition page 148 to record each child's understanding of concepts covered in this lesson.

Science Songs and Poems

> ## Objective
> Children will:
> - Sing a song to develop oral language.
> - Understand that land and water cover Earth.
>
> **You need:** Flip Chart page 37, dinosaur puppet

1 Build Background

Begin a discussion about land and water by asking children what they know about land. (Possible answer: Land has many different shapes.) **Why is water important to living things?** (It helps living things grow.)

2 What to Do

- Tell children that they will learn a song today. Have children listen as you hum the tune of "Oats, Peas, Beans, and Barley Grow." Hum a few times and then invite children to hum along with you.

- When children are ready, sing "Land and Water Cover Earth" to the tune of "Oats, Peas, Beans, and Barley Grow." Sing the verse several times, inviting children to sing with you.

- Direct children's attention to Flip Chart page 37 and have children discuss the picture. Prompt children as needed with questions.

- Then sing the song again using "Annie" the dinosaur puppet.

- Discuss the song by asking children what things cover Earth. (Land and water) **What is water used for?** (Possible answer: Drinking) **What else do we use water for?** (Possible answer: Washing) **What is land used for?** (Possible answer: Growing things)

3 Talk About It

- Point to the word *land* in the song. Say the word and have children repeat it after you. Tell children that land is part of the Earth's surface that is not water. Point to the word *water* in the song. Say the word and have children repeat it after you. Explain that water is the liquid that falls as rain and makes up the Earth's oceans, rivers, lakes, and ponds.

- Invite volunteers to use each word in their own sentences.

You may also wish to teach children the following poems and finger plays with these lessons.

(Lesson 19)

My Bonnie Lies Over the Ocean

My Bonnie lies over the ocean,
My Bonnie lies over the sea.
My Bonnie lies over the ocean,
Oh, bring back my Bonnie to me.

Bring back, bring back,
Oh, bring back my Bonnie to me, to me
Bring back, bring back,
Oh, bring back my Bonnie to me.

(Lesson 20)

Working on the Land

First the farmers plow the land,
 (Guide plow down a row.)
Plow the land, plow the land.
First the farmers plow the land,
Then they plant the seeds.
 (Plant seeds.)

First the builders smooth the land,
 (Make smoothing motion with hands.)
Smooth the land, smooth the land.
First the builders smooth the land,
Then they build a house.
 (Hammer boards together.)

(Lesson 21)

Recycle, Reduce, Reuse

Recycle paper!
Recycle cans and bottles, too!
Recycle! Recycle!
It's something you can do!

Reduce your use of paper!
Use the front and back, too!
Reduce! Reduce!
It's something you can do!

Reuse boxes!
Reuse tins and bottles, too!
Reuse! Reuse!
It's something you can do!

How can water move?

Objective

Children will:
• Demonstrate that water flows down a slope.

1 Build Background

This activity helps children identify characteristics of sand and soil that makes up Earth's surface.

Managing Time and Materials

Time: 15 minutes
Grouping: small groups

Materials: Flip Chart page 38
eyedropper, cup of water, tray with waxed paper, tape, paper towel

2 What to Do

Engage Display Flip Chart page 38. Read the title aloud. Help children identify the pictured materials. (Eyedropper, tray with waxed paper, water) Ask the question under **Build Background** at the bottom of the Flip Chart page 38. Place objects on the table. Then say: **We will be learning about how water moves.** Have volunteers circle and put an X on the appropriate pictures.

Explore Provide a group of children with a set of materials. Model how to drip water on the paper using the eyedropper. Say: **Hold your tray like a slide. Now look at the water. Tell how the water moves. Where will it go?** Have children place additional drops of water at the top of their tray. Then model how to dry the waxed paper using a paper towel. Hold the tray vertically. Say: **Now look at the water. Does it move faster or slower than when we held the tray like a slide?**

Explain Guide children in describing the results. As they share their observations, record them on chart paper. Help them understand that as water moves downhill, the steeper the slope of the paper, the faster the water moves.

Evaluate Ask: **Where did the water move both times? How did you hold your paper to make the water move faster?** Repeat children's answers using complete sentences. Then have children repeat the sentences after you. Then ask: **Do you think the water on flat paper would flow faster or slower than when we held the paper straight up and down?** (Slower)

Extend Repeat the investigation by having children test their predictions about how water moves on a paper that is placed flat on a table.

3 Discuss the Results

1. **Observe** What can you learn about how water moves? (Possible answer: Water always moves downhill.)

2. **Compare and Contrast** When does water move fast? (It moves most quickly when the paper is held straight up and down.)

Go Further Have children work together to create models of steep mountains, gentle hills, and flat plains out of clay. Have them use an eyedropper to drop water over each "landform." **Does water flow faster down the side of a mountain or a hill? Why?** (Water flows faster down a mountain because the sides of mountains are steeper than the sides of hills.) **What happens to water that falls on the flat plains? Why?** (It doesn't move because plains are flat.) Repeat children's responses using complete sentences.

Process Skills

Tell children that they can make **observations** when they look to see how water moves when it is dropped. Explain that they are **collecting data** by making these observations when the paper is held in different ways.

Where is water on Earth?

Objectives

Children will:
- Identify bodies of water.
- Describe the characteristics of bodies of water.

You need: Flip Chart pages 37, 39, globe

Build Background

Display a globe and explain that it shows what Earth looks like. Point out the areas of water and the areas of land and have children note their colors. Have volunteers finger trace around large bodies of water. Explain that these big bodies of water are called *oceans*. Help children to see that there is more water on Earth than there is land.

Circle Time!

Sing "Land and Water Cover Earth"
- Bring children to the circle by singing the song on Flip Chart page 37.
- As children come to the circle and sit, track the words on the chart with your finger and encourage children to sing along. Sing the song again once everyone is sitting.

Vocabulary

ice: frozen water

sea: the great body of salt water; ocean

lake: a body of water with land all around it; a body of fresh water

river: a large natural stream of water that flows into a lake or ocean

Talk About It!

- Use Flip Chart page 39 to review vocabulary terms before you begin to teach Lesson 19.
- Guide **oral vocabulary** development by asking the following questions: **Have you ever gone swimming at an ocean or at a lake? Did the water feel warm or cool? Have you ever crossed a river on a bridge? What did the river look like?** Remind children to answer using complete sentences.

Learn About It!

- Use Teacher Instructions at the bottom of Flip Chart page 39. Children should understand that water can be found in many places on Earth, and that there are many types of water. Point out that ocean water tastes salty while the water in most lakes tastes fresh. **What kind of water would most rivers have?** (Fresh) Explain that small bodies of water called *streams* flow into rivers; very small lakes are called *ponds*.
- Have children use the picture clues and answer the questions. Expand on

children's responses by using complete sentences. Prompt children to repeat your sentences.

- Call on volunteers to circle the ice and put an X on the lake.
- Continue questioning by asking: **If you had a very small boat would you sail it on the ocean or on a lake? Why?** (On a lake so you could stay close to shore)
- Have children explain their answer for the **Compare** question. (Rivers and lakes are bodies of water. A river is larger than a lake.)

Differentiate Instruction

Full Day or Extended Instruction

- Have children work at the sand table. Provide scoops, plastic spoons, and other implements. Make a plastic tub of water available with plastic cups. Then have small groups model one body of water. Once they have finished excavating, show them how to scoop water from the tub to fill their body of water.
- As children work, circulate and have children name the body of water they are modeling, and tell about some of its characteristics.

Reteaching and English Language Learner Support

- Revisit the terms *ice, ocean, lake, river,* and *sea* by showing children a picture of each word. Help children name each picture.
- Give simple clues about characteristics of different bodies of water. For example: **This is the largest body of water on Earth. What is it?** (Ocean or sea) Have children name the correct body of water.

Monitor Progress

- Use "Talk About It," "Learn About It," and Centers activities to check children's progress through the week.
- Refer to "Differentiate Instruction" for reteaching tips.
- Use Assessment Sheet on Teacher's Edition page 148 to record each child's understanding of concepts covered in this lesson.

Science Centers

Center 1: Science Song "Land and Water Cover Earth"
Play the song for the children. Encourage children to sing along. Provide each child with a copy of the song to track words, illustrate, and take home to share, as appropriate.

Center 2: Cross-Curricular Link

Health Tell children that people need to drink water every day especially when it is hot or when they are playing hard. Have children pantomime activities when they might drink water, such as playing a game of tag. As children pantomime, have others guess the activity.

Center 3: Science Journal

Ask children to draw pictures of themselves having fun at a nearby body of water in their **Discovery Journal.** Have children dictate a word or a sentence about their picture.

Lesson 20

How do people use land?

Objective

Children will:
- Describe how people use land to meet their needs.

You need: Flip Chart pages 37, 40

Build Background

Display several wooden toys and ask: **What is this toy made of?** Then have them look around the classroom and name other things that are made of wood. Explain that wood comes from trees that grow on the land.

Circle Time!

Sing "Land and Water Cover Earth"

- Bring children to the circle by singing the song on Flip Chart page 37.

- As children come to the circle and sit, track the words on the chart with your finger and encourage children to sing along. Sing the song again once everyone is sitting.

Vocabulary

build: to make something by putting different materials together

wood: trees cut up into logs and boards for use

Talk About It!

- Use Flip Chart page 40 to review vocabulary terms before you begin to teach Lesson 20.

- Guide **oral vocabulary** development by asking the following questions: **What kinds of food can we grow on land?** (Vegetables, grain) **What kinds of buildings do people build on land?** (Houses, office buildings, etc.) **What kind of materials do people use to build houses?** (Wood, brick, stone) Remind children to answer using complete sentences.

Learn About It!

- Use Teacher Instructions at the bottom of Flip Chart page 40 to guide the science lesson. Children should understand that people use land in many different ways. Land is used to build houses, buildings, and roads. Land is also used to grow plants that can be used for food and for building materials.

- Have children use the picture clues and answer the questions. Expand on children's responses by using complete sentences. Prompt children to repeat your sentences.

- Call on volunteers to circle and put an X on the appropriate pictures.

- Continue questioning by asking: **Why do farmers need to take care of the land?** (To make sure that it can grow plants)
- Have children answer the **Draw Conclusions** question by telling how builders use land and its resources to build.

Differentiate Instruction

Full Day or Extended Instruction
- Take children on a walk around the school to look at building materials. Help them notice where wood is used to build walls, floors, and furniture, Discuss where wood comes from. Point out examples of brick, stone, gravel, and sand if possible.

Reteaching and English Language Learner Support
- Display Flip Chart page 40 and have children point to the picture that shows how farmers use the land. Have them point to the picture that shows how builders use the land.

- Have children answer these questions? **What do farmers do? How do they use the land? What do builders do? How do they use the land?**

Science Centers

Center 1: Science Song "Land and Water Cover Earth"
Play the song for the children. Encourage children to sing along. Provide each child with a copy of the song to track words, illustrate, and take home to share, as appropriate.

Center 2: Cross-Curricular Link
Art Have children use modeling clay to "build" a house, building or some structure found on land. Call on volunteers to tell about their buildings.

Center 3: Science Journal
Ask children to draw pictures of themselves either using the land (Planting a garden), or using something that comes from the land (Wooden toy). Have children dictate a word or a sentence about their picture.

Monitor Progress

- Use "Talk About It," "Learn About It," and Centers activities to check children's progress through the week.
- Refer to "Differentiate Instruction" for reteaching tips.
- Use Assessment Sheet on Teacher's Edition page 148 to record each child's understanding of concepts covered in this lesson.

Lesson 21

How can we help care for Earth?

Objectives

Children will:
- Understand the terms *reuse*, *recycle*, and *reduce*.
- Explain the importance of resource conservation.

You need: Flip Chart pages 37, 41, pencils and crayons

Build Background

Display classroom materials such as pencils and crayons. Ask: **Should we throw these crayons and pencils away after using them once? Why?** Explain that we can reuse many things instead of throwing them away. Point out that to reuse means "to use something again." Have children look around the classroom and identify other things they reuse.

Circle Time!

Sing "Land and Water Cover Earth"
- Bring children to the circle by singing the song on Flip Chart page 37.
- As children come to the circle and sit, track the words on the chart with your finger and encourage children to sing along. Sing the song again once everyone is sitting.

Vocabulary

reuse: to use something again

recycle: to change a product so that it can be used again

reduce: to use less of something

protect: to preserve something or to keep it safe

Talk About It!

- Use Flip Chart page 41 to review vocabulary terms before you begin to teach Lesson 21.
- Guide **oral vocabulary** development by asking the following questions: **What does a light switch do?** (Turns lights off and on) **What is the blue bin used for?** (To recycle) **Where would these things go if they were not collected for recycling?** (In the garbage) **What would that do to Earth?** (Make more trash; pollute the Earth) Remind children to answer using complete sentences.

Learn About It!

- Use Teacher Instructions at the bottom of Flip Chart page 41. Help children to understand that when people reuse and recycle materials, they reduce trash and litter.

- Have children use the picture clues and answer the questions. Expand on children's responses by using complete sentences. Prompt children to repeat your sentences.

- Call on volunteers to circle and put an X on the appropriate pictures.

- Continue questioning by asking: **What could you do to reduce how much water you use?** (Don't let it run when brushing your teeth; take showers instead of baths.) **How do recycling and reusing help protect Earth?** (By recycling and reusing things you use fewer things and throw away less.)

- Have children explain their answer for the **Draw Conclusions** question. (Accept all reasonable responses such as shoeboxes for storage, buttons)

Differentiate Instruction

Full Day or Extended Instruction

- Take children down to the lunchroom to see how lunchroom workers recycle containers. Alternatively, invite a school custodian to talk with children about how the school recycles materials.

- The group can also work together to make posters to display in the classroom, hallways, and lunchroom to remind others in the school how to reuse, recycle, and reduce their use of resources. Once children have illustrated their posters, have them dictate captions for you to record.

Reteaching and English Language Learner Support

- Display several objects, such as a pencil, an empty plastic water bottle, and a small box. Have children point to things that can be reused or recycled.

- Display a container with a recycling logo. Have children tell what the logo means and explain why it is important to recycle things.

Monitor Progress

- Use "Talk About It," "Learn About It," and Centers activities to check children's progress through the week.

- Refer to "Differentiate Instruction" for reteaching tips.

- Use Assessment Sheet on Teacher's Edition page 148 to record each child's understanding of concepts covered in this lesson.

Science Centers

Center 1: Science Song "Land and Water Cover Earth"
Play the song for the children. Encourage children to sing along. Provide each child with a copy of the song to track words, illustrate, and take home to share, as appropriate.

Center 2: Cross-Curricular Link
Art Provide children with a variety of clean and empty recycled materials such as juice cans, small milk cartons, newspaper, old magazines, fabric scraps, ribbon, yarn, old buttons, crayons, paste, and scissors. Have children use these materials to create pencil or crayon holders. When children share their finished objects, have them identify the reused materials that they used.

Center 3: Science Journal
Ask children to draw a picture of themselves doing something to help care for Earth. Have children dictate a word or a sentence about their picture.

Activity

How can you reuse something?

Objective
Children will:
• Demonstrate that some things can be reused in new ways.

1 Build Background

Remind children that when we reuse things, we use things again in a new way. Ask children to name things that they reuse at home, such as shoe boxes, buttons, old socks, plastic containers, and plastic milk containers. As they name each material, have them describe its original use and its new use.

Managing Time and Materials

Time: 20 minutes
Grouping: individuals

Materials: Flip Chart page 42
plastic water bottle, paper shapes, glue, small decorative objects (buttons, fabric strips, bottle caps)

Advance Preparation: Collect clean plastic water bottles of various shapes and sizes and small decorative objects such as buttons and bottle caps. Precut shapes and strips from colored paper and fabric.

2 What to Do

Engage Display Flip Chart Page 59. Read the title aloud as you track the text. Help children identify the pictured materials. (Plastic bottle, shapes, glue, buttons, fabric strips, bottle caps) Point out that the plastic bottle shown in the materials list was originally a water bottle. **What do we usually do with plastic bottles that we use for water or juice?** Help children realize that these bottles are often collected to be recycled. **What other ways could you reuse a plastic bottle?** Then point out the picture on the Flip Chart of the vase made from the plastic bottle.

Explore Tell children that they will investigate how a plastic bottle can be used to make a vase. Say: **Before you begin to <u>investigate</u> how a plastic water bottle can be used to create a vase, you need to <u>make a plan</u> about how you will decorate your bottle.** Focus attention on the vase on the Flip Chart and ask: **What materials were reused to turn this bottle into a vase? What materials would you like to use to decorate your bottle? How will you arrange them on your bottle?** Have children select the materials they would like to use. Once they have planned how to arrange them, have them glue them in place.

Explain Invite children to display their finished vases. Ask: **What did you make with your plastic bottle?** (A vase) **What do you plan to do with it?** (Take it home and use it for flowers.)

Evaluate Have children list the materials they used to make their vases. **Which materials were reused?** (The plastic bottle, buttons, fabric, colored paper, and bottle caps)

Extend Review the other ways that plastic bottles could be reused. Have children choose one use and come up with a plan describing how they would make the project; for example, they could make a weighted game spinner or a doorstop by filling an empty plastic bottle with sand and decorating the outside with markers. If possible, have children complete the project.

3 Discuss the Results

1. **Draw Conclusions** What did you learn about reusing objects by doing this investigation? (Possible answer: Instead of throwing something out, it may be possible to reuse it in a different way.)

2. **Compare** How are all the vases alike? How are they different? (Possible answers: All the vases were made by reusing materials. They are decorated in different ways.)

Go Further Provide children with clean empty cans, colored paper, shapes cut from colored paper and fabric, and glue. Display the materials and ask: **How could you reuse an empty can to make a pencil holder?** (You could cover it with colored paper and decorate it with shapes.) Once children have made a plan, have them follow it to create pencil holders. Encourage them to take their vases and pencil holders home and tell family member how they reused objects to make something useful.

Process Skills

Tell children that they were **observing** when they told how they reused an object to make something new. Explain that they were **investigating** when they made a plan and tried it out.

Listening and Speaking Tip

• As children share their vases, remind them to look at the audience when they speak. Suggest that they point out an interesting feature of their design or an unusual way that they reused materials.

Notes

Unit C Physical Science

Introduce the Unit

- Introduce the unit of Physical Science by showing children Flip Chart page 43. Discuss with children what they see in the photograph by asking:

- **What things do you see in this classroom?** Call on volunteers, in turn, to circle each object you name.

- Then point to an object and have children identify it and its color.

- **What object would you use to draw a picture?** Have a volunteer put an X on an object. Continue with other volunteers.

- **What object would you use to make something?** Have a volunteer put an X on an object. Continue with other volunteers.

- **What do you like about this classroom?**

- Encourage children to share what they know about the things they see in the classroom.

- Explain to children that in this unit, they will learn about why some things are grouped together, how things change, and why we use tools.

Introduce the Floor Puzzle

- Tell children that they will put together a puzzle that looks just like the photograph on Flip Chart page 43.

- Place the puzzle pieces on the floor and invite children to work as a group to put the puzzle together. Tell them that they can use the photograph on the flip chart to help them. Provide assistance as needed.

- As children are working on the puzzle, ask the following questions:
  Where is the easel in the photograph?
  What is on the wall?
  What color is the table?

- Explain to children that the puzzle will be in the Science Center. They will have other opportunities to put the puzzle together again and discuss the picture on the puzzle as they learn more about **Physical Science.**

Unit C: Physical Science

Materials List for Unit C

Activities	Kit materials	School-supplied materials
What can you tell about some things? pp. 112–113	balloon plastic spoon plastic cup wooden block	water
What will stay on top of water? pp. 122–123	plastic spoon rock plastic bowl wooden block sponge craft stick	water pencil
How can we make things move? pp. 132–133	plastic cup rubber ball wooden block toy car plastic tray	crayon books
What tool can you use to talk to a friend? pp. 140–141	string paper cups paper clips	pencil (teacher use) scissors (teacher use)

Unit C Bibliography

Teachers may want to share the following books with children to expand their comprehension of science concepts taught in Unit C.

You may wish to place some or all of these books in the Science Center after reading them aloud to children.

Air Is All Around You
by Franklyn M. Branley
[HarperCollins, ISBN 0-06-445148-8,1996]
This book helps children to understand that air is all around.

Alfred's Camera
by David Ellwand
[Dutton Children's Books, ISBN 0-525-45978-2, 1998]
This picture book puzzle follows Alfred, a dog, in his search for his camera. Each page is filled with many objects in different sizes and shapes. **Challenge**

I Love Trains
By Philemon Sturges
[HarperCollins, ISBN 0-06-028901-5, 2001]
This book provides simple facts about the many uses of trains.

My Magnet
by Robert Pressling
[Gareth Stevens Publishing, ISBN 0-8368-1117-8,1994]
This book explains how magnets work and why they work on some objects and not others. **Challenge**

Pop! A Book About Bubbles
by Kimberly Brubaker Bradley
[HarperCollins, ISBN 0-06-445048-1,1986]
This book explains why soap bubbles are round, and why they pop.

Solid, Liquid, or Gas?
by Sally Hewitt
[Childrens Press, ISBN 0-516-20794-6,1998]
At the bottom of each page is a simple activity or questions regarding a familiar object. **Challenge**

Solid, Liquid, or Gas?
by Fay Robinson
[Childrens Press, ISBN 0-516-06041-4,1995]
This book introduces the concept of matter. **Challenge**

Tractor
By Craig Brown
[Greenwillow Books, ISBN 0-688-10500-9, 1995]
This story tells about a farmer and the equipment he uses.

What Makes a Magnet?
by Franklyn M. Branley
[HarperCollins, ISBN 0-06-445148-8,1996]
This book explains how a magnet works and provides activities for making both a compass and a magnet. **Challenge**

Unit C: Planning Guide

Lesson/Activity	Pacing	Science Objectives/Vocabulary
Activity What can you tell about some things? pp. 112–113	15 minutes	Children will explore the properties of solids, liquids, and gases.
22 How can you sort objects? pp. 114–115	20 minutes	Children will identify observable properties of objects. size, color, shape, sound, heavy, light
23 What different kind of sounds can you hear? pp. 116–117	20 minutes	Children will identify sounds. loud, soft, high, low
24 What is a solid, a liquid, and a gas? pp. 118–119	20 minutes	Children will name the three different forms of matter: solids, liquids, gases. liquid, solid, gas
Activity What will stay on top of water? pp. 122–123	15 minutes	Children will demonstrate that some objects stay on top of the water and others go to the bottom.
25 How can solids and liquids change? pp. 124–125	20 minutes	Children will demonstrate that solids and liquids can be changed. cut, bend, mix, fold, melt, freeze
26 Does it sink or float? pp. 126–127	20 minutes	Children will understand that solids can sink and float. sink, float

Lesson/Activity	Pacing	Science Objectives/Vocabulary
27 What can a magnet do? pp. 128–129	20 minutes	Children will understand that magnets attract some metal objects. magnet, metal, pull
Activity How can we make things move? pp. 132–133	20 minutes	Children will understand that a push or a pull can be used to make an object move.
28 How do some objects move? pp. 134–135	20 minutes	Children will understand that objects move in different ways. push, back, forth, up, down, roll
29 Is it fast or slow? pp. 136–137	20 minutes	Children will tell about the motion of objects at different speeds. fast, slow
30 What are some tools? pp. 138–139	20 minutes	Children will identify a variety of tools. hammer, scissors, rake, pencil
Activity What tool can you use to talk to a friend? pp.140–141	20 minutes	Children will use a paper cup and string "telephone" to explore how sound travels.
ASSESSMENT pp. 149–151		

Science Songs and Poems

> ## Objective
> Children will:
> • Sing a song to develop oral language.
> • Understand the meaning of *sort*.
> • Identify observable properties of objects.
>
> **You need:** Flip Chart page 44, dinosaur puppet, red crayon, red construction paper, red counter, rectangular shaped-block and chalkboard eraser

1 Build Background

Begin a discussion about sorting by placing a red counter, a red crayon, and a red sheet of paper on a table. Ask: **How are these objects alike?** (They all are red.) Explain that some things can go together because they are alike in some way. Then hold up a rectangular block and a chalkboard eraser. **How are these objects alike?** (They have the same shape.)

2 What to Do

• Tell children that they will learn a song today. Have children listen as you hum the tune of "Old MacDonald." Hum a few times and then invite children to hum along with you.

• When children are ready, sing "Sort It!" to the tune of "Old MacDonald." Sing the verse several times, inviting children to sing with you.

• Direct children's attention to Flip Chart page 44 and have children discuss the picture. Prompt children as needed with questions.

• Then sing the song again using "Annie" the dinosaur puppet.

• Discuss the song by asking children what questions they could ask to help sort objects. Prompt them as needed by reading the questions from the song.

3 Talk About It

• Point to the word *sort* in the title of the song. Say the word and have children repeat it after you. Tell children that the word *sort* means "to group things that are alike in some way." Invite volunteers to find and circle the word *sort* in the song.

- Have children complete these sentences: "We can sort the crayons by _____." (Color) "We can sort the beads by _____." (Color, shape, size)

You may also wish to teach children the following poems and finger plays with these lessons.

(Lesson 22)
Describing Things

Look at an apple. Describe it to me.
It is red? Is it round? Is it hard?
Red, round, hard—an apple is all three.

Look at a lemon. Describe it to me.
Is it yellow? Is it rough? Is it sour?
Yellow, rough, sour—a lemon is all three.

(Lesson 23)
The Big Bass Drum

Oh! We can play on the big bass drum,
And this is the way we do it;
Rub-a-dub, boom goes the big bass drum,
And this is the way we do it.

Additional verses:
Oh! We can play on the violin, …
Zum, zum, zin says the violin, …
(Repeat drum sound.)

Oh! We can play on the little flute, …
Tootle, toot, toot says the little flute, …
(Repeat violin and drum sounds.)

(Lessons 24–25)
My Red Balloon

I had a little red balloon
(Make ball with hands)
And I blew and blew and blew,
(Blow into ball three times)
Until it grew and grew and grew.
(Move hands apart)
I tossed it in the air,
(Pretend to toss ball)
And never let it drop.
(Shake head)
I bounced it on the ground,
(Pretend to bounce ball)
Until it suddenly went "POP!"
(Clap hands loudly)

What can you tell about some things?

Objectives
Children will:
- Describe the properties of different objects.
- Explore the properties of solids, liquids, and gases.

1 Build Background

This activity allows children to explore different kinds of matter and the specific properties of each kind of matter.

Managing Time and Materials

Time: 15 minutes
Grouping: whole group

Materials: Flip Chart page 45
cup of water, balloon, plastic spoon, block, safety goggles

2 What to Do

Safety Tip
- Children should wear safety goggles before handling balloons.

Engage Display Flip Chart page 45. Read the title aloud as you track the text. Help children identify the pictured materials. (Cup of water, balloon, plastic spoon, block) Then focus attention on the block. Ask: **What can you tell me about this block? How does it feel when you <u>touch</u> it? Tell us what shape it has. Do you think it is heavy or light? What do you think would happen to the shape of this block if I dropped it on the desk?** After you drop the block, have children observe it and tell if their predictions about what would happen were correct.

Explore Ask a volunteer to hold up the glass of water. Call another volunteer forward and say: <u>**Touch**</u> **the water and <u>tell</u> us what you feel. Does the water feel wet or dry?** Then call on another volunteer to stir the water with the spoon. **What happens when the water is stirred? What do you think would happen to the shape of this water if I poured a little bit on the table?** After you do so, have children observe the water and tell if their predictions were correct. Explain that water takes the shape of the glass when it is in the glass. Have children describe what shape water has when it is poured on the table.

Next, blow air into the balloon. Ask: **What did I put into the balloon? How did the balloon's shape change when I put air into the balloon?** Tie the neck of the balloon and have volunteers gently squeeze it. **What do you feel when you squeeze the balloon?** (Air) **What do you think is moving around inside the balloon? What do you feel as I open the neck of the balloon?**

Explain Guide children in describing the results. Ask: **Which thing is hard and does not change its shape when it is dropped?** (The block) **Which thing is wet and can be stirred and poured and takes the shape of what it is in?** (Water) **Which thing cannot be seen but can be felt and can make other things change their shape?** (Air)

Evaluate Display a hard rubber ball and drop it. Ask: **Is this more like the block, the water, or the air in a balloon? Why?** (Possible answer: It is more like the block because it keeps its shape when it is dropped.) Repeat children's answers using complete sentences. Then have children repeat the sentences after you.

Extend Provide plastic containers of other shapes and sizes and have children observe what happens when they pour the same amount of water into these containers. Discuss that even though the water level is different in each container, the amount of water is the same. Guide them to see this is so because water takes the shape of its container.

3 Discuss the Results

1. **Observe** What did you learn about objects when you dropped, poured, or pushed against them? (Possible answer: Some hard things, like blocks, do not change their shape. Other things like water or the air do change their shape when you pour them or when you push against them.)

2. **Infer** Do you think the air in a balloon takes up space? How do you know? (Yes; when a balloon is empty, it is flat. When you put air in the balloon, it pushes out the sides of the balloon; it is taking up space.)

Go Further Display a balloon filled with helium and another balloon filled with air. Tie strings to the balloons and then attach them to the backs of a chair. Have children observe what happens when you release the two balloons. Ask: **Which of these balloons do you think is lightest?** (The balloon floating up.) **What does this tell you about the air or gas in these balloons?** (They are different. One is heavier than the other.)

Process Skills

Tell children that they are **observing** when they watch what happens to objects when they are dropped, poured, or pushed. Explain that they are **communicating** when they share their observations with others.

Listening and Speaking Tip

• Remind children that when they speak in front of the class, it is important to look at their listeners and keep their hands away from their mouths as they talk. Remind them to speak slowly and clearly as they tell about what they observe.

How can you sort objects?

Objectives

Children will:
- Identify observable properties of objects.
- Sort objects into groups based on their properties.

You need: Flip Chart pages 44 and 46, red counter, red construction paper

Build Background

Remind children that they know that objects are made of different things. Explain that objects can also be the same in many ways. Display a red counter and a piece of red construction paper. Ask: **How are these objects alike?** (They are the same color.) **How are these objects different?** (Possible answer: They are different shapes and sizes.)

Circle Time!

Sing "Sort It!"
- Bring children to the circle by singing "Sort It!" on Flip Chart page 44.
- As children come to the circle and sit, track the words on the chart with your finger and encourage children to sing along. Sing the song again once everyone is sitting.

Talk About It!

- Use Flip Chart page 46 to review vocabulary terms before you begin to teach Lesson 22.

- Guide **oral vocabulary** development by asking these questions: Point to each object in turn and ask: **What color is this object? Who can name another object in the picture that is the same color?** Point to the yo-yo and say: **This yo-yo has a round shape. Who can name something that has a square shape?** (Green pillow) Point to the drum and say: **You can make sounds with this drum.** Point to the pillow. **This pillow is very light, which means it does not weigh a lot. Who can name something that is heavy?** (Drum, book) Remind children to answer using complete sentences.

Learn About It!

- Use Teacher Instructions at the bottom of Flip Chart page 46 to guide the science lesson. Children should understand that they can put objects together that are alike in some way. This is called *sorting*.

Vocabulary

size: how big or how small something is

color: red, yellow, blue or any combination of them

shape: the way something looks

sound: something that you hear

heavy: weighing a lot

light: not weighting very much

- Have children use the picture clues and answer the questions. Call on volunteers to circle and put an X on the appropriate pictures.
- Continue questioning by asking the following: **What objects would belong in a group of small green objects?** (The green pencil and the green ball)
- Have children share their answer for the **Classify** question. (By size)

Differentiate Instruction

Full Day or Extended Instruction
- Display a wide assortment of classroom objects on a table. Make sure the objects are different colors, weights, sizes, textures, and shapes. Then display sorting rings or lengths of yarn tied together to make a ring. Explain that they will work together to place objects inside each ring that are the same in one important way.
- After all the objects are sorted by color ask: **How are all the objects in this group alike?** Repeat this procedure to have children sort objects by weight, by size, by texture, and by shape. Point out that depending on how things are being sorted, the same object can go into different groups.

Reteaching and English Language Learner Support
- Reinforce the words *size, color, shape, sound, heavy,* and *light* by displaying a group of objects and saying, **Point to something red in color. Point to something big in size,** and so on. Then have children sort the objects on Flip Chart page 46 by color or size.

Monitor Progress
- Use "Talk About It," "Learn About It," and Centers activities to check children's progress through the week.
- Refer to "Differentiate Instruction" for reteaching tips.
- Use Assessment Sheet on Teacher's Edition page 149 to record each child's understanding of concepts covered in this lesson.

Science Centers

Center 1: Science Song "Sort It!"
Play "Sort It!" for the children in the listening center. Encourage children to sing along. Provide each child with a copy of the song to track words, illustrate, and take home to share, as appropriate.

Center 2: Cross-Curricular Link
Math Provide children with buttons, blocks, or other small objects that are different colors and different sizes. Model how to use the objects to make a pattern, such as alternating red and blue blocks. Have children sort the objects by color, size, or shape and then use the sorted objects to create a pattern.

Center 3: Science Journal
Have children draw two objects that are the same color.

Lesson 23

What different kinds of sounds can you hear?

Objectives

Children will:
• Identify what sound is.
• Describe the properties of sounds.

You need: Flip Chart pages 44, 47, picture of roaring lion

Build Background

Display a picture of a roaring lion. Tell children to imitate the lion's sound. Ask: **Does the lion make a loud sound or a soft sound when it roars?** Discuss why animals make loud sounds. (Possible answer: To warn other animals; to call to other animals)

Circle Time!

Sing "Sort It!"

• Bring children to the circle by singing "Sort It!" on Flip Chart page 44.

• As children come to the circle and sit, track the words on the chart with your finger and encourage children to sing along. Sing the song again once everyone is sitting.

Vocabulary

loud: not a soft sound
soft: not a loud sound
high: pitch; not low
low: pitch; not high

Talk About It!

• Use Flip Chart page 47 to review vocabulary terms before you begin to teach Lesson 23.

• Guide **oral vocabulary** development by asking these questions: **What kind of sound does the bird make? Is this a low sound or a high sound?** (High) **What kind of sound does the bullfrog make? Is this a low sound or a high sound?** (Low) **What kind of sound does a siren make?** (Loud) **Why do you think ambulances have loud sirens?** (So they can be heard from far away) **Could you hear this clock ticking from far away? Why not?** (It has a soft sound.) Remind children to answer using complete sentences.

Learn About It!

• Use **Teacher Instructions** at the bottom of Flip Chart page 47 to guide the science lesson. Guide children to name each object and describe the sound that it makes. Point out that a sound travels through the air and is something you hear. Have children lightly rest their hands on a drum or piano as you play it. Ask them to tell what they feel. Explain that the sounds

Sound

All sounds are caused by vibrations, and the speed of sound depends on the medium through which it travels. The pitch of a sound (whether it is high or low) is determined by its frequency—the number of vibrations a sound wave makes in one second. The volume of a sound (whether it is loud or soft) is determined by its amplitude—the amount of energy carried by the sound waves.

Monitor Progress

• Use "Talk About It," "Learn About It," and Centers activities to check children's progress through the week.

• Refer to "Differentiate Instruction" for reteaching tips.

• Use Assessment Sheet on Teacher's Edition page 149 to record each child's understanding of concepts covered in this lesson.

they heard were made by what they felt. Pluck a stretched rubber band or flex and release a ruler. Point out that the back and forth movement they see is called vibration.

• Have children use the picture clues and answer the questions. Call on volunteers to circle and put an X on the appropriate pictures.

• Continue questioning by asking the following: **What body part do you use to hear sounds?** (You use your ears to hear sounds.)

• Have children explain their answer for the **Classify** question. (Accept all reasonable responses.)

Differentiate Instruction

Full Day or Extended Instruction

• Lead children on a listening walk around the school or in the neighborhood. As you walk, have them identify high, low, soft, and loud sounds and tell what is making each sound.

• On your return to the classroom, display different objects that make sounds. Help children sort the objects by sound. Have children name the objects that make a loud sound; soft sound; high sound; low sound.

Reteaching and English Language Learner Support

• Reinforce the words loud, soft, high, and low by displaying pictures of different instruments. Ask questions such as: **Which instrument makes a loud sound?** Have children respond by pointing to the instrument and repeating the type of sound.

• Have children summarize the lesson by completing these sentences: "The _____ makes a loud sound." "The _____ makes a soft sound." "The _____ makes a high sound." "The _____ makes a low sound."

Science Centers

Center 1: Science Song "Sort It!"

Play "Sort It!" for the children in the listening center. Encourage children to sing along. Provide each child with a copy of the song to track words, illustrate, and take home to share, as appropriate.

Center 2: Cross-Curricular Link

Math Tell children that they can make patterns with sound. Clap out several patterns using loud and soft claps and help children "read" the pattern. Repeat each pattern several times and have children extend it with you. You can also do this activity with rhythm instruments. Once children understand how sound patterns can be made, have them create their own. Tape record these patterns and then play them back for the group.

Center 3: Science Journal

Have children close their eyes and listen for sounds. Have them draw something that is making one of the sounds that they hear.

What is a solid, a liquid, and a gas?

Objectives

Children will:
- Name the three different forms of matter: solids, liquids, and gases.
- Identify solids, liquids, and gases.
- Describe the properties of solids, liquids, and gases.

You need: Flip Chart pages 44, 48, pinwheel, dinosaur puppet

Build Background

Display a pinwheel and blow on it. **What is making this pinwheel move? What is air? Can you see air?** Then have children blow on their hands. **What did you feel? What does this tell you about air?** (Possible answer: You can feel air. It tells you that air can move.)

Circle Time!

Sing "Sort It!"

- Bring children to the circle by singing "Sort It!" on Flip Chart page 44.

- As children come to the circle and sit, track the words on the chart with your finger and encourage children to sing along. Sing the song again once everyone is sitting using the dinosaur puppet.

Vocabulary

liquid: something that flows like water; it has no shape of its own

solid: something that has its own shape

gas: something that has no size or shape of its own; it can expand

Talk About It!

- Use Flip Chart page 48 to review vocabulary terms before you begin to teach Lesson 24.

- Guide **oral vocabulary** development. Point to a colored block on the chart. **What would happen to this solid if I dropped it on the floor?** (Nothing; still have its same shape) **What happens to a liquid like water when you pour it into containers of different sizes and shapes?** (Water takes the shape of the container.) **What happens to the air when it is put inside balloons or balls of different shapes or sizes?** (Takes shape of object) Remind children to answer using complete sentences.

Learn About It!

- Use **Teacher Instructions** at the bottom of Flip Chart page 48 to guide the science lesson.

Science Misconception

Gases

Children may confuse the gas that is put in a car with the gas that is one of the states of matter. Tell children that the gas we put in a car is actually called *gasoline*, which is a liquid. Explain that when we use the word *gas* to talk about this liquid, we are just shortening the word *gasoline*.

• Children should understand that everything around them is made up of *matter*. Point to the solids and explain that a solid has its own shape that does not change. Put a pencil inside a cup. **What happened to the shape of the pencil when I put it in a cup?** (The pencil's shape does not change.) Tell children that water is a liquid that is wet. Explain that liquids take up space by taking the shape of their container. Pour water into several different containers. **What happened to the shape of the liquid?** (It changed depending on the shape of the container.) Explain that air is a gas that cannot be seen but it does take up space like a liquid. Blow up several balloons that have different shapes. **What happened to the gas in these balloons?** (It changed shape depending on the shape of the balloon.)

• Have children use the picture clues and answer the questions. Call on volunteers to circle and put an X on the appropriate pictures.

• Continue questioning by asking the following: **Suppose I show you a cup filled with water. What is the solid and what is the liquid?** (The cup is a solid. The water is a liquid.) Have children share their answer for the **Classify** question. (Solid)

Differentiate Instruction

Full Day or Extended Instruction

• Provide children with old magazines and scissors. Then divide them into three groups. Help one group find pictures of solids, another group to find pictures of liquids, and a third group to find pictures of things that contain gases, such as tires, balls, and empty containers. Then call on children, in turn, to hold up their picture and tell about it using the appropriate word: *liquid, solid,* or *gas.*

Reteaching and English Language Learner Support

• Have children complete these sentences: "A _____ is something that keeps its own shape." "A _____ is something that is wet and takes the shape of its container." "A _____ is something you cannot see; however, it takes the shape of its container."

Science Centers

Center 1: Science Song "Sort It!"
Play "Sort It!" for the children in the listening center. Encourage children to sing along. Provide each child with a copy of the song to track words, illustrate, and take home to share, as appropriate.

Center 2: Cross-Curricular Link
Writing Remind children that wind is moving air and that air is made of gases. Talk with children about how they can tell that air is moving. Then have them dictate sentences about the wind. Write their sentences on chart paper.

Center 3: Science Journal
Have children draw something filled with gas. Then have children, in turn, show and tell about their picture.

Monitor Progress

• Use "Talk About It," "Learn About It," and Centers activities to check children's progress through the week.

• Refer to "Differentiate Instruction" for reteaching tips.

• Use Assessment Sheet on Teacher's Edition page 150 to record each child's understanding of concepts covered in this lesson.

Science Songs and Poems

> ## Objective
> Children will:
> - Sing a song to develop oral language.
> - Understand that an activity involves some action
>
> **You need:** Flip Chart page 49, dinosaur puppet

1 Build Background

Begin a discussion about activities by reminding children of some of the science activities they were involved with. Explain that an activity involves doing something.

2 What to Do

- Tell children that they will learn a song today. Have children listen as you hum the tune of "Skip to My Lou." Hum a few times and then invite children to hum along with you.

- When children are ready, sing "Activity Day" to the tune of "Skip to My Lou." Sing the verse several times, inviting children to sing with you.

- Direct children's attention to Flip Chart page 49 and have children discuss the picture. Prompt children as needed with questions.

- Then sing the song again using "Annie" the dinosaur puppet.

- Discuss the song by asking children what is melting in the sun. (Ice) **What things does the magnet pull?** (Paper clips)

3 Talk About It

- Point to the word *activity* in the song. Say the word and have children repeat it after you. Explain that *activity* means "doing something or some kind of action."

- Invite volunteers to complete this sentence: "An activity that I like to do is _____." (Accept any reasonable response.)

You may also wish to teach children the following poems and finger plays with these lessons.

(Lesson 26)

Little boat floats
bob, bob, bob,
gently on top of the sea.
(Make floating and bobbing motions with hands.)

Little sub sinks
glub, glub, glub,
down to the bottom of the sea.
(Make diving motions with hands.)

(Lesson 27)

Buttons and bows,
Nails and tacks;
What kind of things
Will a magnet attract?

Things of some metals,
Like pins and pails.
Things made of iron,
Like pots and nails.

Activity

What will stay on top of water?

Objective

Children will:
- Demonstrate that some objects stay on top of water while other objects go to the bottom.

1 Build Background

This activity helps children to identify solid objects that go to the bottom of water or stay on top of water.

Managing Time and Materials

Time: 15 minutes
Grouping: whole group

Materials: Flip Chart page 51
bowl of water, block, pencil, sponge, rock, cube

2 What to Do

Engage Display Flip Chart page 51. Read the title aloud as you track the text. Help children identify the pictured materials. (Bowl of water, wooden block, pencil, sponge, marble, rock) Ask: **Which of these objects are liquids? Which of the objects are solids? What do you <u>predict</u> would happen if we put each of these objects in the bowl of water? Which objects would stay on top of the water? Which objects would go to the bottom of the water?** As children make their predictions, encourage them to tell why they think as they do. Record their predictions next to each object's name in the first column of a two-column chart. Then based on these predictions, have children sort the objects into two groups.

Explore Tell children that they will check their <u>predictions.</u> **We will check to see which objects stay on top of the water and which go to the bottom of the water.** Call on volunteers to take turns selecting one object and placing it in the bowl of water. Say: <u>Tell</u> **what you observe.**

Explain Guide children in describing their observations. Ask: **Which objects stayed on top of the water?** (The block, the pencil, the sponge) **Which objects went to the bottom of the water?** (The rock and the cube) After children describe each test, help them record the results in the second column of the chart.

Evaluate Have children use the chart to compare their predictions to the observations they made during the experiment. **Which of your predictions were correct? Which predictions were not correct?** (Answers will depend on children's predictions.)

Extend Provide other classroom objects and ask children to make predictions about whether they will stay at the top of the water or whether they will go to the bottom. Through discussion, guide children to see that weight and size do not always matter in whether an object stays at the top or goes to the bottom of the water. Model this by showing that a heavy wooden block will stay on top of the water while a rock will go to the bottom. Point out that what the object is made of helps determine what happens to it in water.

3 Discuss the Results

1. **Observe** did you learn about objects by doing this experiment? (Possible answer: Some objects stay on the surface of the water, and some objects go to the bottom of the water.)

2. **Predict** Do you predict a pair of metal scissors would stay on the top of water? How could you test this? (No, metal scissors will not stay on top of the water. You could test this by doing an experiment of putting the scissors in water to observe what happened.)

Go Further Provide children with pieces of clay and a piece of aluminum foil. Have them roll a clay ball and see what happens when they place the clay ball in water. Then help children fold the aluminum foil into a flat shape and place it in water. Ask: **What happens when you put the foil in water?** (It stays on top of the water.)

Process Skills

Tell children that they are **predicting** when they tell what they think will happen. Point out that they are **communicating** when they tell what happens to objects.

Listening and Speaking Tip

• Remind children to ask for help if their experiment is not working correctly. Tell them to politely raise their hand and wait for you to call on them if help is needed.

Lesson 25

How can solids and liquids change?

Objectives

Children will:

- Demonstrate that solids can be changed by cutting, folding, bending, and melting.
- Demonstrate that liquids can be changed by freezing or melting.

You need: Flip Chart pages 44 and 49, sheet of paper

Build Background

Display a sheet of paper. **Is this paper a solid or a liquid?** (A solid) **What can you do to the paper to change it?** (Possible answers: Cut, fold, bend, and color it) Demonstrate these actions and display the results. **Is this still paper?** (Yes.)

Circle Time!

Sing "Sort It!"

- Bring children to the circle by singing "Sort It!" on Flip Chart page 44.
- As children come to the circle and sit, track the words on the chart with your finger and encourage children to sing along. Sing the song again once everyone is sitting.

Vocabulary

cut: to separate

bend: to change shape

mix: to put things together and blend them well

fold: to double over on itself

melt: to turn something from a solid into a liquid by heating it

freeze: to become hard from cold

Talk About It!

- Use Flip Chart page 49 to review vocabulary terms before you begin to teach Lesson 25.
- Guide **oral vocabulary** development by asking these questions: **Have you ever put powdered paint into water and mixed it up with a spoon? What happens to the paint?** (It becomes a liquid.) **Is a fruit pop a solid or a liquid when you take it out of the freezer? What happens if you leave a frozen fruit pop on a plate in the sun? How does it change?** (It melts.) **When you fold or cut paper, is it still paper, or does it change into something else?** (Still paper) **How has the straight pipe cleaner been changed?** (It is bent.) Remind children to answer using complete sentences.

Learn About It!

- Use **Teacher Instructions** at the bottom of Flip Chart page 49 to guide the science lesson. Children should understand that solids may be cut, bent, and mixed without changing. Solids can also be mixed with other solids and with liquids. Sometimes when this happens, it changes the solids. Solids can also be melted when heat is applied. When this happens, the solid changes into a liquid. Liquids can be mixed with other liquids or with solids. Liquids can also be frozen. When a liquid is frozen, it turns into a solid.

- Have children use the picture clues and answer the questions. Call on volunteers to circle and put an X on the appropriate pictures.

- Continue questioning by asking the following: **Where could I put water to have it freeze and change from a liquid to a solid?** (You could put it in a freezer.) **What would happen to the ice cubes in my glass if I left it sitting in the sun?** (The ice cubes would melt.) Have children share their answer for the **Classify** question. (Solid)

Differentiate Instruction

Full Day or Extended Instruction
- Provide children with construction paper, pipe cleaners, pieces of fabric, scissors, and liquid white glue. Hold up each material and have children identify it as a solid or a liquid.

- Have children cut, bend, and fold the materials and paste the pieces on a sheet of colorful construction paper to make a collage. Talk with children about how the materials have changed. **Is the paper still paper? Are the pipe cleaners still pipe cleaners? Is the fabric still fabric? How have you mixed these materials?**

Reteaching and English Language Learner Support
- Reinforce the words *cut, bend, mix, fold* by giving children paper and scissors. Say each word and demonstrate it using scissors and paper. Then draw pictures of a solid ice cube and a melted ice cube. Ask children to point to the picture that shows the word *melt*; *freeze*.

- Have children identify how each pictured object is changing by completing this sentence: "This _____ is being changed by _____."

Monitor Progress
- Use "Talk About It," "Learn About It," and Centers activities to check children's progress through the week.
- Refer to "Differentiate Instruction" for reteaching tips.
- Use Assessment Sheet on Teacher's Edition page 150 to record each child's understanding of concepts covered in this lesson.

Science Centers

Center 1: Science Song "Sort It!"
Play "Sort It!" for the children in the listening center. Encourage children to sing along. Provide each child with a copy of the song to track words, illustrate, and take home to share, as appropriate.

Center 2: Cross-Curricular Link
Cooking Remind children that a liquid can change into a solid. Make jello with children, helping them stir the powdered mixture with water. Pour the jello into a big bowl or jello mold and place in the refrigerator until ready. Have children enjoy jello for a snack!

Center 3: Science Journal
Have children draw a solid that changes into a liquid. Then have them tell about their picture.

Lesson 26

Does it sink or float?

Objectives

Children will:
• Understand that solids can sink or float.

You need: Flip Chart pages 50 and 52, bowl of water, classroom objects

Build Background

Display a bowl filled with water. **Is this water a solid or a liquid? How do you know?** (Water is a liquid because it is wet, takes up space, and because it takes the shape of its container.) Display several classroom objects. **What happens when you put objects into water?** (They will either stay on the top or go to the bottom.) Explain that when something stays on top of the water, we say that it floats. When it goes to the bottom, we say that it sinks.

Circle Time!

Sing "Activity Day"

• Bring children to the circle by singing "Activity Day" on Flip Chart page 49.

• As children come to the circle and sit, track the words on the chart with your finger and encourage children to sing along. Sing the song again once everyone is sitting.

Vocabulary

sink: to go down
float: to move along slowly on top of the water

Talk About It!

• Use Flip Chart page 52 to review vocabulary terms before you begin to teach Lesson 26.

• Guide **oral vocabulary** development by asking these questions: **What shape does the liquid?** (Rectangle) **Which things in this picture are floating?** (Rubber duck, toy boat) **Which things are sinking?** (Rock, shell) Remind children to answer using complete sentences.

Learn About It!

• Use **Teacher Instructions** at the bottom of Flip Chart page 52 to guide the science lesson. Children should understand that an object's weight can give them clues about whether an object will sink or float. Explain that what an object is made of and the shape of the object are also useful clues that they can use. Help children realize that objects filled with air, made of wood, or with a shape that spreads out on the water may float. Objects made of heavy metals, stone, or solid plastic often sink.

Science Misconception

Buoyancy

The ability of an object to float depends on its buoyancy. Buoyancy is determined by several factors—the density of an object, which is how packed together its matter is, and on its shape and the amount of air it contains. Objects with a high density and a compact shape sink because the weight of the object is greater than the weight of the water being displaced.

- Have children use the picture clues and answer the questions. Expand on children's responses by using them in complete sentences. Prompt children to repeat the sentences.

- Call on volunteers to circle and put an X on the appropriate pictures.

- Continue questioning by asking the following: **Why do people wear life jackets when they go out in a boat?** (To help them float if the boat tips over) **Where would you expect to find shells if you visited the ocean? Why?** (You would find them on the bottom of the ocean because shells sink when they are put in water.)

- Have children share their answer for the **Classify** question. (Liquid)

Differentiate Instruction

Full Day or Extended Instruction

- Provide children with old magazines and scissors. Help children cut out pictures of objects that would sink or pictures of objects that would float.

- Set up two charts, one titled **Float** and the other **Sink.** Invite children, in turn, to paste their picture on the appropriate chart and explain their choices.

Reteaching and English Language Learner Support

- Display a container of water with objects that are floating and sinking. Point to each object and have children say the word *sink* or *float* to describe it.

- Encourage children to tell what they know about what can happen to a solid when it is put in water. As part of their explanation, ask them to share the meaning of the terms *sink* and *float*.

Science Centers

Monitor Progress

- Use "Talk About It," "Learn About It," and Centers activities to check children's progress through the week.

- Refer to "Differentiate Instruction" for reteaching tips.

- Use Assessment Sheet on Teacher's Edition page 150 to record each child's understanding of concepts covered in this lesson.

Center 1: Science Song "Activity Day"

Play "Activity Day" for the children in the listening center. Encourage children to sing along. Provide each child with a copy of the song to track words, illustrate, and take home to share, as appropriate.

Center 2: Cross-Curricular Link

Health Ask: **Is a bar of soap a liquid or solid? Do most bar soaps sink or float?** (Sink) Explain that washing your hands often helps get rid of germs, and germs can cause people to get sick. Discuss that people should wash their hands before eating, before cooking, after touching a pet, after playing outside, after doing an art activity. Demonstrate the correct way to wash hands using soap and warm water for about 20 seconds, in order to be an effective germ killer.

Center 3: Science Journal

Have children draw a picture of something that is floating or something that is sinking.

Lesson 27

What can a magnet do?

Objectives

Children will:

· Understand that magnets attract some metal objects.

You need: Flip Chart pages 50 and 53, different sizes and shapes of magnets

Build Background

Display different sizes and shapes of refrigerator magnets. **What are these objects called?** (They are magnets.) **How do people use magnets like this?** (They use them to hang things up on a refrigerator or on metal cabinets.)

Circle Time!

Sing "Activity Day"

· Bring children to the circle by singing "Activity Day" on Flip Chart page 49.

· As children come to the circle and sit, track the words on the chart with your finger and encourage children to sing along. Sing the song again once everyone is sitting.

Vocabulary

magnet: a piece of metal that pulls bits of iron or steel to it; a tool for pulling things

pull: make something move toward you

metal: a hard substance such as iron or steel

Talk About It!

· Use Flip Chart page 53 to review vocabulary terms before you begin to teach Lesson 27.

· Guide **oral vocabulary** development by first pointing to each object pictured on the chart and identifying it with children. Then ask: **What is attached to the magnet?** (Paper clips) **What else do you think will attach to the magnet?** (Safety pin) Remind children to answer using complete sentences.

Learn About It!

· Use **Teacher Instructions** at the bottom of Flip Chart page 53 to guide the science lesson.

· Guide children to tell about objects that a magnet will pull and will not pull to it. Introduce the word *attract*. Explain that *attract* means "to pull something closer." Children should understand that a magnet will attract some kinds of metal.

· Have children use the picture clues and answer the questions. Expand on children's responses by using them in complete sentences. Prompt children to repeat the sentences.

· Call on volunteers to circle and put an X on the appropriate pictures.

- Continue questioning by asking the following: **What could you use to help you quickly pick up a box of spilled paper clips? Why?** (You could use a magnet because it would pull the clips toward it.)
- Have children explain their answer for the **Compare** question. (They are both made of metal. They can be picked up by a magnet.)

Differentiate Instruction

Full Day or Extended Instruction
- Provide children with small classroom objects and a collection of magnets of different shapes and sizes.
- Set up a two-column chart titled with this question: "Will a Magnet Move It?" Title one column **Yes** and the other column **No**.
- Have children begin by predicting what the magnets can move. Have them sort the objects into two piles. Then ask each child to select one object and trace the object on a large sticky note. After the child tests the object with a magnet to see if it will move, have the child tell what happened and attach the sticky note drawing in the correct column. Continue this until all children have had a turn.
- Focus children's attention on all the objects in the **Yes** column. **What is one important way that all these objects are alike?** (They are all made of metal that is pulled or attracted by a magnet.)

Reteaching and English Language Learner Support
- Revisit the terms *pull*, *metal* and *magnet*. Have children pantomime what it means to pull something. Then have them point to things in the classroom that are made of metal.
- Then have children list at least three objects from Flip Chart page 53 that a magnet would pull.

Science Centers

Monitor Progress
- Use "Talk About It," "Learn About It," and Centers activities to check children's progress through the week.
- Refer to "Differentiate Instruction" for reteaching tips.
- Use Assessment Sheet on Teacher's Edition page 150 to record each child's understanding of concepts covered in this lesson.

Center 1: Science Song "Activity Song"
Play "Activity Song" for the children in the listening center. Encourage children to sing along. Provide each child with a copy of the song to track words, illustrate, and take home to share, as appropriate.

Center 2: Cross-Curricular Link
Math Point out that magnets can be used to make games. Have children work together to make fishing poles by attaching a magnet to the end of a meter stick with yarn. Then provide paper fish; each fish has a paper clip fastened to "its nose." Place two fish faceup on the table or on the floor. Using their magnet fishing rods, have children take turns "catching the fish." Help each child count how many fish he/she caught.

Center 3: Science Journal
Have children draw pictures of other ways that we use magnets at home or in the classroom. Encourage them to dictate a sentence about their picture.

Science Songs and Poems

Objective

Children will:
- Sing a song to develop oral language.
- Understand that objects can move in different ways.

You need: Flip Chart page 54, dinosaur puppet, toy truck, ball

1 Build Background

Begin a discussion about how objects move by displaying a toy truck and a ball. **How would we get this toy truck to move?** (Push it) **How would we get a ball to move?** (Roll it)

2 What to Do

- Tell children that they will learn a song today. Have children listen as you hum the tune of "Here We Go Round the Mulberry Bush." Hum a few times and then invite children to hum along with you.

- When children are ready, sing "I Made a Car" to the tune of "Here We Go Round the Mulberry Bush." Sing the verse several times, inviting children to sing with you.

- Direct children's attention to Flip Chart page 54 and have children discuss the picture. Prompt children as needed with questions.

- Then sing the song again using "Annie" the dinosaur puppet.

- Discuss the song by asking children if they ever made a car from a small box. If children have, invite them to tell how they made their car. **How can you make a toy car move?** (Give it a push) **How can you make a toy car go faster?** (Push it with more force or give it a great big push)

3 Talk About It

- Point to the word *race* in the song. Say the word and have children repeat it after you. Tell children that a race is a contest to find out who or what is fastest.

- Invite volunteers to complete this sentence: "My little _____ wins the race!" (Accept any reasonable answer.)

You may also wish to teach children the following poems and finger plays with these lessons.

(Lesson 28)

I Have a Little Wagon

I have a little wagon.
(Hold hand out with the palm up.)
It goes everywhere with me.
(Move hand around.)
I can pull it.
(Pull hand toward you.)
I can push it.
(Push hand away from you.)
I can turn it upside down.
(Turn hand upside down.)

(Lesson 29)

The Top

Wind the top,
(Make winding motion.)
Wind the top,
Round and round and round.
(Spin around several times.)
Now it makes a little hop
(Make a hopping motion.)
And spins along the ground.
(Spin faster.)
Faster, faster, faster,
Whirling, whirling, whirling.
Spinning round and round again,
Twirling, twirling, twirling.
Wobbly, wobbly, wobbly!
(Make a wobbling motion.)
It's running down I fear.
Slower, slower, slower.
(Spin more and more slowly.)
Now it falls! Oh dear!
(Topple over and fall to the floor.)

(Lesson 30)

Scissors

Open then shut,
The scissors cut.
Snip, snip, snip.

Fast then slow,
The scissors go.
Snip, snip, snip.

Activity

How can we make things move?

Objective
Children will:
• Understand that a push or a pull can be used to make an object move.
• Understand that there is a relationship between force and motion.

---

1 Build Background

This activity helps children to observe different forces that can make objects move.

Managing Time and Materials

Time: 20 minutes
Grouping: whole group

Materials: Flip Chart page 55
wooden block, plastic cup, ball, toy car, crayons, two thick books, tray

---

2 What to Do

Engage Display Flip Chart page 55. Read the title aloud as you track the text. Help children identify the pictured materials. (Block, cup, ball, toy car, and a ramp made from books) Ask: **Look at the picture of the ramp made out of books. What do you think would happen if we put a ball at the top of this ramp? What word would you use to describe how it would move? Which of the other objects shown on this page do you predict would roll down the ramp?** As children make their predictions, encourage them to tell why they think as they do. **Do you think these objects would roll more quickly or more slowly if we gave them a push? Why?**

Explore Tell children that they will check their predictions by doing an experiment. Remind them that an experiment is a way of testing objects to see if something is true or not true. Call on volunteers to help you build the ramp. Then have another child select one of the objects and place it at the top of the ramp. **<u>Look</u> at the ball. <u>Tell</u> what you observe when the ball is let go. Did the object move? How did it move?** Repeat this procedure with the remaining objects. If an object will not roll down the ramp by itself, have a volunteer give it a strong push to get it to move.

Explain Guide children in describing their observations. Ask: **What sense did you use to help you figure out how each object moved?** (My sense of sight) **Which objects rolled by themselves?** (The ball and the car) **Which objects needed a push to get them to slide down the ramp?** (The block and the cup)

Evaluate Have children use their hands to demonstrate a rolling motion and then a sliding motion. **What is alike about things that roll and move by themselves?** (They are round in shape.) **What is alike about things that need a push to get them to move?** (They are not round in shape.)

Extend Provide other classroom objects and ask children to make predictions about how they will move down a ramp. Then have children experiment to test their predictions.

3 Discuss the Results

1. **Observe** What did you learn about objects by doing this experiment? (Possible answer: Objects move in different ways. Some objects roll and others slide. Round objects will roll by themselves down a ramp. Objects that are not round need a push to slide down a ramp.)

2. **Predict** What other objects would roll down a ramp? (Possible answers include a pencil, a pen, and a can.) **What objects would need a push to slide down a ramp?** (Possible answers include a book, a bookbag, and a lunchbox)

Go Further Provide children with objects that are round and not round and have them place them on a level table top. **Are these objects moving? What would you have to do in order to get them to move?** Guide children to see that even round things require a push or a pull in order to start them moving when they are on a flat surface. Have children explore using different kinds of force to move an object. **How can you make a ball roll farther?** (You can make it move farther by giving it a harder push.) **How can you make a ball roll more slowly?** (You can make it move more slowly by giving it a gentle push.)

Process Skills

Tell children that they are **observing** when they watch what happens when an object is placed at the top of the ramp. Explain that they are **predicting** when they tell whether or not they think the object will move and how it will move.

Listening and Speaking Tip

• Remind children that they should use their inside voices when they are working with a partner or in a small group. Remind them that when they are sharing their answers with the class, they should speak clearly and loudly enough to be heard by everyone in the class.

How do some objects move?

Objectives

Children will:
- Understand that objects can move in different ways and in different directions.

You need: Flip Chart pages 54, 56, picture of a wagon

Build Background

Display a picture of a wagon. **If you stand in front of this wagon and hold on to the handle, what do you have to do to make the wagon move?** (You have to pull it.) **If you stand behind the wagon and put your hands on the back, what do you have to do to make the wagon move?** (You have to push it.) Explain that pushes and pulls are two things we can do to make an object move.

Circle Time!

Sing "I Made a Car"
- Bring children to the circle by singing "I Made a Car" on Flip Chart page 54.
- As children come to the circle and sit, track the words on the chart with your finger and encourage children to sing along. Sing the song again once everyone is sitting.

Talk About It!

- Use Flip Chart page 56 to review vocabulary terms before you begin to teach Lesson 28.

- Guide **oral vocabulary** development by asking these questions: **What objects on Flip Chart page 56 can move? Imagine you are swinging on this swing. Use your hand to show how the swing moves. What words tell about this movement? Pretend you are playing with a yoyo. How does a yoyo move on the string? Use your hand to show this movement.** Remind children to answer using complete sentences.

Learn About It!

- Use Teacher Instructions at the bottom of Flip Chart page 56 to guide the science lesson.

- Guide children to tell about the direction that each object moves. Point

Vocabulary

push: to move something away from you

back: to move backward

forth: to move forward

up: to move something from a lower place to a higher place

down: to move something from a higher place to a lower place

roll: to move along by turning over and over

Science Misconception

Forces

Nonliving things need to be pushed or pulled into action. They do not move on their own. Pushes and pulls are called forces. The wind is a force that may push a door shut. Gravity is a force that pulls things downwards towards Earth.

out that the direction tells how something is moving. Model how to use direction words such as *straight, zigzag, up, down, back,* and *forth.* Explain that things can also be moved into different places. Explain that a place tells where something is. Guide them to use words such as *above, below, in front of, behind, over, under, in, out, left or right* to describe the place where a thing moves.

- Have children use the picture clues and answer the questions. Expand on children's responses by using them in complete sentences. Prompt children to repeat the sentences.

- Call on volunteers to circle and put an X on the appropriate pictures.

- Continue questioning by asking the following: **How does a ball move when it is bounced?** (It moves up and down.)

- Have children explain their answer for the **Sequence** question. (Push it or roll it)

Differentiate Instruction

Full Day or Extended Instruction

- Distribute pictures from coloring books that show objects or people moving in different ways: *push, back, forth, up, down, roll, pull,* and so on.

- Have children color their picture, hold it up, and talk about it using the correct "movement" word.

Reteaching and English Language Learner Support

- Give children a small classroom object. Then give oral directions using the words *push, back, forth, up, down,* and *roll.* Have children follow the directions by moving the object.

- Have children take turns giving directions telling their classmates how to move. In their directions, have them use the words *push, pull, back, forth, up, down, roll,* and *slide.*

Monitor Progress

- Use "Talk About It," "Learn About It," and Centers activities to check children's progress through the week.

- Refer to "Differentiate Instruction" for reteaching tips.

- Use Assessment Sheet on Teacher's Edition page 151 to record each child's understanding of concepts covered in this lesson.

Science Centers

Center 1: Science Song "I Made a Car"

Play "I Made a Car" for the children in the listening center. Encourage children to sing along. Provide each child with a copy of the song to track words, illustrate, and take home to share, as appropriate.

Center 2: Cross-Curricular Link

Physical Education Lead children in a game of "Simon Says" in which you use motion and direction words that tell children how to move; for example: **Swing your arms back and forth.** Keep children in the game even when they make an error.

Center 3: Science Journal

Have children draw a picture of themselves playing their favorite playground game or activity. Have them dictate a sentence telling how they are moving.

Lesson 29

Is it fast or slow?

Objectives

Children will:

• Tell about the motion of objects at different speeds.

You need: Flip Chart pages 54, 57, picture of a car

Build Background

Invite two volunteers to come to the front of the class. Have one child walk slowly while the other child walks quickly. Say: **These children are walking at different speeds. Speeds tells us how fast or how slow something is moving. Which child walks fast? Which child walks slowly? Which child will take longer to walk all the way across the room?** (The child who is walking slowly.)

Circle Time!

Sing "I Made a Car"

• Bring children to the circle by singing "I Made a Car" on Flip Chart page 54.

• As children come to the circle and sit, track the words on the chart with your finger and encourage children to sing along. Sing the song again once everyone is sitting.

Vocabulary

fast: moving quickly
slow: moving with less speed than others

Talk About It!

• Use Flip Chart page 57 to review vocabulary terms before you begin to teach Lesson 29.

• Guide **oral vocabulary** development by asking these questions: **What words would you use to tell about how these objects move?** (*Fast, slow*) **Suppose you could go someplace by train or by tricycle. Which would be a slower way to go? Why?** (Tricycle because it doesn't have a motor) Remind children to answer using complete sentences.

Learn About It!

• Use **Teacher Instructions** at the bottom of Flip Chart page 57 to guide the science lesson. Children should understand that objects can move at different speeds. If an object moves fast, it is quick. If an object is slow, it is not fast.

• Have children use the picture clues and answer the questions. Expand on children's responses by using them in complete sentences. Prompt children to repeat the sentences.

• Call on volunteers to circle and put an X on the appropriate pictures.

- Continue questioning by asking the following: **What is something that moves faster than a train?** (Possible answer: a plane or a helicopter)
- Have children explain their answer for the **Infer** question. (Motorcycle because it has a motor)

Differentiate Instruction

Full Day or Extended Instruction
- Make a class list of things that move fast or slow with the children.
- Then name an object on the list and talk about how the object moves. Continue with other objects.
- Have children look at all the pictures on the "Fast" chart and select the object that they think moves fastest of all. Encourage them to give reasons to explain their responses. Repeat this procedure for the "Slow" chart.

Reteaching and English Language Learner Support
- Revisit the terms *fast* and *slow* by having children walk around the classroom at a very fast pace. Then have them move around very slowly. Have them use the words *fast* and *slow* to describe their actions.
- Have children look at Flip Chart page 57 again. Have them complete this sentence to tell how each thing moves. "The _____ moves _____."

Science Centers

Center 1: Science Song "I Made a Car"
Play "I Made a Car" for the children in the listening center. Encourage children to sing along. Provide each child with a copy of the song to track words, illustrate, and take home to share, as appropriate.

Center 2: Cross-Curricular Link
Social Studies Talk with children about methods of transportation that people use to get from place to place. Discuss which transport methods are used on or under land, which are used on water, and which are used in the air. Have children find and cut out pictures of different types of transport in old magazines. Have children, in turn, hold up a picture and tell about it, describing how it moves.

Center 3: Science Journal
Have children draw a picture of a fast object. Have them dictate a sentence about their picture.

Monitor Progress
- Use "Talk About It," "Learn About It," and Centers activities to check children's progress through the week.
- Refer to "Differentiate Instruction" for reteaching tips.
- Use Assessment Sheet on Teacher's Edition page 151 to record each child's understanding of concepts covered in this lesson.

Lesson 30

What are some tools?

> **Objectives**
>
> Children will:
> - Identify a variety of tools.
> - Understand how tools are used.
> - Classify tools into different groups.
>
> **You need:** Flip Chart pages 54, 58, hand lens

Build Background

Display a hand lens. **What is this tool? How does it work?** (It makes things look larger.) **How do we use this tool to help us observe?** (We use a hand lens to help us see things more clearly.) Point out that a tool is anything that helps us do work. Invite children to look around the classroom and name other tools they see.

Circle Time!

Sing "I Made a Car"
- Bring children to the circle by singing "I Made a Car" on Flip Chart page 54.
- As children come to the circle and sit, track the words on the chart with your finger and encourage children to sing along. Sing the song again once everyone is sitting.

Vocabulary

hammer: a tool used for driving nails

scissors: a tool for cutting things

rake: a long-handled tool used for gathering leaves

pencil: a pointed tool used for writing or drawing

Talk About It!

- Use Flip Chart page 58 to review vocabulary terms before you begin to teach Lesson 30.

- Guide **oral vocabulary** development by asking these questions: **What objects do you see? As each object is identified, ask: What do we use it for?** Then have children tell how they use each object. Remind children to answer using complete sentences.

Learn About It!

- Use **Teacher Instructions** at the bottom of Flip Chart page 58 to guide the science lesson. Children should understand that tools come in all shapes and sizes. Some tools are very complicated, and other tools are very simple, but all tools help us do work.

- Have children use the picture clues and answer the questions. Expand on children's responses by using them in complete sentences. Prompt children to repeat the sentences.

- Call on volunteers to circle and put an X on the appropriate pictures.

- Continue questioning by asking the following: **What is a tool that can help you clean your room?** (Possible answer: a broom, a dust mop, a vacuum cleaner) **In what ways are scissors, a saw, and a knife alike?** (They are all tools that are used for cutting.)
- Have children explain their answer for the **Compare** question. (They are tools we use to help us eat food.)

Differentiate Instruction

Full Day or Extended Instruction
- Place an assortment of tools on the table. Make sure that they are different sizes and shapes and are used for different purposes.
- Invite each child to select a tool. Have the child name the tool and describe how it is used.
- Then help children categorize the tools into groups by asking: **Which tools are large? Which tools are small? Which tools are used to help you cut? Which tools are used to help you cook? Which tools are used to help you draw? Which tools are used to build things?**
- Conclude the activity by asking children to explain why tools are important. (Tools make work easier.)

Reteaching and English Language Learner Support
- Revisit the terms *hammer*, *scissors*, *rake*, and *pencil* by displaying each object or a picture of it. Have children point to each tool as you name it.
- Display various tools and have children identify each and tell what it can do by completing these sentences: "This is a _____." "It can _____."

Monitor Progress
- Use "Talk About It," "Learn About It," and Centers activities to check children's progress through the week.
- Refer to "Differentiate Instruction" for reteaching tips.
- Use Assessment Sheet on Teacher's Edition page 151 to record each child's understanding of concepts covered in this lesson.

Science Centers

Center 1: Science Song "I Made a Car"
Play "I Made a Car" for the children in the listening center. Encourage children to sing along. Provide each child with a copy of the song to track words, illustrate, and take home to share, as appropriate.

Center 2: Cross-Curricular Link
Writing Place an assortment of tools on a table. Hold up each tool and help children identify it. Then call on volunteers to choose a tool and dictate or write a sentence about it. Prompt children with questions as needed.

Center 3: Science Journal
Have children draw a picture of their favorite tool. Have them explain their picture.

Activity

What tool can you use to talk to a friend?

Objective

Children will:
• Use a paper cup and string "telephone" to explore how sound travels.

1 Build Background

Talk with children about times they have used the telephone. Explain that telephones allow us to talk to people who are not close by. If possible, display a toy telephone or a real telephone. Have children identify where they listen to hear sounds and where they speak to transmit sounds.

Managing Time and Materials

Time: 20 minutes
Grouping: pairs

Materials: Flip Chart page 59
plastic cups, strong string, small paper clips or buttons, scissors and sharpened pencil for teacher use

Advance Preparation: Before the activity, assemble a string telephone for each pair of children. Use the pencil to make a small hole in the bottom of each cup and thread the string through the hole. Tie each end of the string to a paper clip to secure it within the cup.

2 What to Do

Engage Display Flip Chart page 59. Read the title aloud as you track the text. Display one of the telephones you have assembled and help children identify the materials as paper cups, a string, and paper clips. Ask a child to help you demonstrate how the phone works. Ask: **What do you <u>predict</u> you will hear if you hold the other cup to your ear while I am talking into my cup?**

Explore Tell children that they will check their predictions by doing an activity. Pair children and give them each a phone. Say: **Stand far enough apart so the string is <u>pulled</u> tight. Then <u>listen</u> as the other person <u>talks</u>.** After each turn, have children share their partner's message. Then have children vary the volume of their voices, reminding them not to shout. Have them test how loudly they must whisper in order for their partner to hear the words. Then have pairs of children move closer together.

What happens to the string? (It goes slack.) **What happens to your partner's voice?** (It can't be heard.) Point out that their voice causes the cup to vibrate. The taut string allows these vibrations to travel along the string to their partner's cup and then to their ear.

Explain Guide children in describing their observations. Ask: **How does the sound travel from one cup to another?** (It travels along the string.) **What happens when the string is not pulled tightly?** (The sound cannot travel along the string.) **Why is it easier to hear a louder rather than a softer sound?** (A louder sound travels better than a softer sound along the string.)

Evaluate Have children **summarize** by describing step-by-step how sound travels through a paper cup telephone from the speaker to the listener. (The speaker speaks into the paper cup. These sounds make the cup vibrate. These vibrations travel through the string to the other paper cup. The vibrations from this paper cup make the listener's ear vibrate.)

Extend Have children repeat the experiment while grasping the taut string stretched between the phones. Through discussion, guide them to see that their hand prevents the string from vibrating, or quickly moving back and forth, which means that sounds cannot travel along the string.

3 Discuss the Results

1. **Observe** What happens when the string is tight and when it is loose? (When it is tight, sounds travel along the string. When it is loose, sounds do not travel along the string.)

2. **Compare** Which sounds are easier to hear through your telephone? (Louder sounds are easier to hear than very soft sounds.)

Go Further To help children see the movements that vibrations cause, provide a toy drum and have children sprinkle dried beans or cereal on top of the drum head. Have them lightly tap the drum. Ask: **What happens to the beans when you tap the drum?** (They move up and down.) **How does this movement change when you tap the drum harder?** (They move farther.) Then place a hand on the drum head to dampen the vibrations as a child taps the drum again. **What happens to the beans when you tap the drum with your hand on the drum head?** (The beans hardly move.) Point out that anything that interferes with sound vibrations makes sounds more difficult to hear.

Process Skills

Tell children that they **observe** when they describe the sounds they hear when the string is in different positions. Explain that when they use a home-made paper cup telephone to talk to a partner, they are **using a model** of a

Notes

Assessment for Unit A, Lessons 1-4

Name_____

Date_____

Rubric for Skills & Behavior

	Emerging	Proficient	Exceeds Targeted Expectations
Follows directions			
Listens attentively			
Participates orally			
Works cooperatively			

Learning Objectives Checklist

Observe each child as he or she engages in discussion of concepts and activities. Use the following observation checklist to take notes as he or she learns new concepts.

Child:

Names the five senses.

Explains how the senses help people learn about living and nonliving things.

Identifies and compares living and nonliving things.

Identifies the needs of living things.

Describes what living things can do.

Yes   No

Teacher Observations

_____

_____

_____

Assessment for Unit A, Lessons 5-8

Name_____

Date_____

Rubric for Skills & Behavior

	Emerging	Proficient	Exceeds Targeted Expectations
Follows directions			
Listens attentively			
Participates orally			
Works cooperatively			

Learning Objectives Checklist

Observe each child as he or she engages in discussion of concepts and activities. Use the following observation checklist to take notes as he or she learns new concepts.

Child: Yes   No

Identifies different kinds of plants.

Explains that plants need air, water, light, and space to grow.

Identifies four parts of a plant.

Describes different plant habitats.

Identifies the stages in the life cycle of a flowering plant.

Teacher Observations

_____

_____

_____

Assessment for Unit A, Lessons 9-10

Name_____

Date_____

Rubric for Skills & Behavior

	Emerging	Proficient	Exceeds Targeted Expectations
Follows directions			
Listens attentively			
Participates orally			
Works cooperatively			

Learning Objectives Checklist

Observe each child as he or she engages in discussion of concepts and activities. Use the following observation checklist to take notes as he or she learns new concepts.

Child:

Identifies different types of animals.

Describes distinguishing characteristics of insects, birds, fish, and reptiles.

Identifies different ways that animals move.

Explains how different body parts help different animals move.

Yes   No

Teacher Observations

_____

_____

_____

Assessment for Unit A, Lessons 11-12

Name_____

Date_____

Rubric for Skills & Behavior

	Emerging	Proficient	Exceeds Targeted Expectations
Follows directions			
Listens attentively			
Participates orally			
Works cooperatively			

Learning Objectives Checklist

Observe each child as he or she engages in discussion of concepts and activities. Use the following observation checklist to take notes as he or she learns new concepts.

Child:

Identifies similarities and differences between adult animals and their young.

Describes ways animals change as they grow.

Describes different animal habitats.

Explains ways different characteristics enable animals to live in different habitats.

Yes **No**

Teacher Observations

_____

_____

_____

Assessment for Unit B, Lessons 13-15

Name_____

Date_____

Rubric for Skills & Behavior

	Emerging	Proficient	Exceeds Targeted Expectations
Follows directions			
Listens attentively			
Participates orally			
Works cooperatively			

Learning Objectives Checklist

Observe each child as he or she engages in discussion of concepts and activities. Use the following observation checklist to take notes as he or she learns new concepts.

Child:

Identifies and describes the characteristics of different kinds of weather.

Explains how changes in the weather affect people's lives.

Chooses clothing appropriate for the weather.

Identifies the four seasons.

Describes the weather and other characteristics of each season.

Yes   No

Teacher Observations

_____

Assessment for Unit B, Lessons 16-21

Name_____

Date_____

Rubric for Skills & Behavior

	Emerging	Proficient	Exceeds Targeted Expectations
Follows directions			
Listens attentively			
Participates orally			
Works cooperatively			

Learning Objectives Checklist

Observe each child as he or she engages in discussion of concepts and activities. Use the following observation checklist to take notes as he or she learns new concepts.

Child: **Yes**   **No**

Explains that land and water cover Earth's surface.

Identifies that land is made up of rocks, soil, and sand.

Identifies and describes characteristics of landforms.

Describes the day and night sky and identifies objects in each.

Identifies and describes characterisitics of bodies of water.

Describes ways people use land to meet their needs.

Gives examples of the terms *reuse*, *recycle*, and *reduce*.

Teacher Observations

_____

Assessment for Unit C, Lessons 22-23

Name_____

Date_____

Rubric for Skills & Behavior

	Emerging	Proficient	Exceeds Targeted Expectations
Follows directions			
Listens attentively			
Participates orally			
Works cooperatively			

Learning Objectives Checklist

Observe each child as he or she engages in discussion of concepts and activities. Use the following observation checklist to take notes as he or she learns new concepts.

Child:

Identifies observable properties of objects, such as size, color, shape, sound, and mass.

Sort objects into groups based on their properties.

Identifies that a sound is something that is heard.

Describes the properties of different sounds.

Yes   No

Teacher Observations

_____

_____

_____

Assessment for Unit C, Lessons 24-27

Name _____

Date _____

Rubric for Skills & Behavior

	Emerging	Proficient	Exceeds Targeted Expectations
Follows directions			
Listens attentively			
Participates orally			
Works cooperatively			

Learning Objectives Checklist

Observe each child as he or she engages in discussion of concepts and activities. Use the following observation checklist to take notes as he or she learns new concepts.

Child:

	Yes	No
Explains that matter exists as solids, liquids, and gases.		
Identifies and describes the properties of solids, liquids, and gases.		
Describes how solids can be changed by cutting, folding, bending, and melting.		
Describes how liquids can be changed by freezing.		
Identifies solid objects that float and sink.		
Explains that magnets attract some metal objects.		

Teacher Observations

_____

Assessment for Unit C, Lessons 28-30

Name_____

Date_____

Rubric for Skills & Behavior

	Emerging	Proficient	Exceeds Targeted Expectations
Follows directions			
Listens attentively			
Participates orally			
Works cooperatively			

Learning Objectives Checklist

Observe each child as he or she engages in discussion of concepts and activities. Use the following observation checklist to take notes as he or she learns new concepts.

Child:

Explains that a push or a pull can make objects move.

Describes differences in the ways that objects move.

Describes differences in the direction and speed that objects move.

Identifies a variety of tools and explains how they are used.

Classifies tools into different groups by use.

Yes   No

Teacher Observations

_____

_____

School to Home Letter

Here are the key concepts we learned in Unit A, Life Science:

- Objects have different shapes, sizes, and textures.
- We have five senses and each sense helps us learn about living and nonliving things.
- Plants, animals, and people are living things.
- Objects are nonliving things.
- All living things need food, air, and water to live.
- Animals and people can grow and move.
- There are many different kinds of plants.
- Plants grow in many kinds of places.
- Roots, stem, leaves, and flower are parts of a plant.
- Insects, birds, fish, and reptiles (lizards) are animals.
- Animals move in different ways.
- Some baby animals look like their parents.
- Animals live in different places.

Vocabulary Review
Your child learned these vocabulary words.

Lesson 1: **hear, taste, touch, see, smell**

Lesson 2: **animal, living, nonliving, plant**

Lesson 3: **air, food, shelter, water**

Lesson 4: **grow, move, crawl**

Lesson 5: **bush, grass, tree, vegetable**

Lesson 6: **flower, leaf, roots, stem**

Lesson 7: **desert, farm, forest, garden**

Lesson 8: **fruit, seed, seedling, soil**

Lesson 9: **insect, bird, fish, lizard, wings, fins**

Lesson 10: **hop, fly, run, swim**

Lesson 11: **alike, different**

Lesson 12: **ocean, land, cold**

Take-Home Activities

- Place some objects on a table such as a plastic glass, ball, towel, and pencil. Ask your child to choose one object and tell something about it by looking at it. Then have your child touch the object and tell something else about the object. Continue with each object.

- Together with your child look through magazines and storybooks for pictures of animals. Help your child name the animal and then ask your child to tell what covers the animal, how the animal moves, and whether the animal might live in a cold place, in the water (ocean, pond, river, lake), or on land.

School to Home Letter

Here are the key concepts we learned in Unit B, Earth Science:

- The temperature may be different in different locations.
- Weather can change from day to day and from place to place.
- People wear different kinds of clothes in different weather.
- There are four seasons.
- In many places, the weather changes in each season.
- Land is made up of rocks, sand, and soil.
- There are many different kinds of places on Earth.
- The night sky and the day sky look different.
- The Sun gives us light during the day.
- There is more water on Earth than there is land.
- People use land to meet their needs.
- People need to help care for Earth.

Vocabulary Review

Your child learned these vocabulary words.

Lesson 13: **sunny, rainy, windy, snowy, cloudy**

Lesson 14: **clothes, outside, hot, warm**

Lesson 15: **summer, winter, fall, spring**

Lesson 16: **rocks, Earth, soil**

Lesson 17: **mountain, valley, plain, canyon**

Lesson 18: **Moon, stars, Sun, day, night, sky**

Lesson 19: **ice, sea, frozen, lake**

Lesson 20: **build, wood**

Lesson 21: **reuse, recycle, reduce, protect**

Take-Home Activities

- Using an outdoor thermometer, help your child read the temperature in a sunny spot and a shady spot. Ask: **Which spot was warmer? Which spot was colder? Why?**

- Look at soil and sand samples together with your child. (If possible, provide a magnifying glass.) Display at least two different soil samples on newspaper or paper plates. Using a plastic spoon, have your child describe the color, texture, and smell of each soil. If sand is available, have your child compare the sand to the soil samples.

School to Home Letter

Here are the key concepts we learned in Unit C, Physical Science:

- Objects can be sorted based on their properties.
- Sounds can be loud, low, soft, and high.
- Different things make different sounds.
- A liquid takes the shape of its container.
- Air is all around us.
- A solid has its own shape and size.
- Solids can be changed by cutting, folding, bending, and melting.
- Solids can sink or float.
- Magnets can attract some other metal objects.
- Objects can move in different ways.
- Objects can move at different speeds.
- People use different tools to help them do work.

Vocabulary Review

Your child learned these vocabulary words.

Lesson 22: **size, color, shape, sound, heavy, light**

Lesson 23: **low, soft, high, loud**

Lesson 24: **liquid, solid, gas**

Lesson 25: **cut, bend, fold, mix, melt, freeze**

Lesson 26: **sink, float**

Lesson 27: **pull, metal, magnet**

Lesson 28: **push, roll, back, forth, up, down**

Lesson 29: **fast, slow**

Lesson 30: **hammer, scissors, rake, pencil**

Take-Home Activities

- Provide a bowl of water, a wooden block, pencil, sponge, plastic toy, rocks, and other objects. Have your child hold up each object and predict whether it will sink or float in the water. Then have the child put the object in the water and discuss the results.

- Explore with your child how a push or pull can be used to make an object move. Assemble two thick books, a toy car, a small ball, a plastic cup, and a small box or block. Help your child make a ramp from books or use building materials such as blocks. Ask your child to pick an object and place it at the top of the ramp. Discuss what you both observe as the object goes down the ramp. Decide if the object moved and how it moved.

Index